PORTRAIT OF JAIME

Jaime's rich relatives had always ignored her, and she had had no time for them. Now, belatedly, her grandfather had sent for her—presumably to bury the hatchet. Should she go—especially as it would mean she would be seeing far too much of the overwhelming Quinn Sterling?

BLACK INGO

Ingo Faulkner was a devastatingly attractive man,
even to Genny who had known him all her life,
and he made no secret of the fact that he was fas-
cinated by her. But attraction wasn't love, was it?
Wasn't Genny simply heading for trouble if she
took him seriously?

ONE-WAY TICKET

Jay MacCallister was the Boss, the forceful one of
the MacCallister family; his word was law—and
his magnetism was undeniable. His younger
brother David was rather less forceful—but it was
David that Melanie Kent had come to Australia
to marry, and she had better keep reminding herself of that fact . . .

SWANS' REACH

Rachael was heartbroken at having to leave her
lovely old home, Swans' Reach, and she would
probably have hated anyone who bought it. But
she felt an extra special antipathy to Dominic
Retford, with his dark good looks and his air of
being monarch of all he surveyed. Never, she
said, could they be friends. But she could be
wrong . . .

THE MAN ON HALF-MOON

Katharine's brother Darin had disappeared,
somewhere in Queensland, and she could not rest
until she had gone up there to see if she could
find him. But the problem of Darin's whereabouts
paled into insignifance in the face of the much
greater problem of how to cope with his boss, the
ruthless—and devastatingly attractive—Curt
Dangerfield!

PORTRAIT OF JAIME

BY

MARGARET WAY

MILLS & BOON LIMITED
17-19 FOLEY STREET
LONDON W1A 1DR

First published 1977
Philippine copyright 1977
This edition 1977

© Margaret Way 1977

Set in Linotype Plantin 11 on 11½ pt

ISBN 0 263 72508 1

Made and printed in Great Britain by
Richard Clay (The Chaucer Press), Ltd., Bungay, Suffolk

CHAPTER ONE

JAIME didn't know her father had a visitor. She came up from the beach, her hair a slick wet rope over one shoulder, her face and her slender body tanned to an even gold, lightly glistening with sea water. There was something about this visit she didn't know about, and the first pang of apprehension struck her. No one, except Tavia, came to the beach house without an invitation. The gallery handled her father's work and most of his clients. She glanced at the Mercedes parked in the driveway and made a wry face to herself, stopping abruptly to slip her beach coat over her brief swimsuit. It was well after four, and the beach was deserted, incredibly beautiful in the late afternoon sunlight. She turned at the top of the stairs and looked back at it.

Her life had been an endless procession of hideaways; the silent inland, the bush and the mountains. She hadn't always liked them, but because she loved her father she had always kept silent. Here she loved best of all. The eternal summer of Queensland, the blue and the gold. It was a picture that would never be erased from her mind. Here, too, her father seemed happiest and painted best of all. He might never make the national galleries, but he was more than just a competent professional artist. He had very real style and a lyrical quality that helped him escape mediocrity. His landscapes and seascapes, the occasional portrait and still life, found a ready market among collectors who demanded decorative professionalism at moderate prices. In any event, his painting and pottery had been his sole source of income for ten years now. If there was no money for luxuries, they lived comfortably enough in an arrangement Derry Gilmore fondly imagined suited both of them, with Jaime as his dedicated unpaid housekeeper and assistant, herself with an artistic potential he consciously avoided. Jaime was the only person on earth Derrick Gilmore, a charming, deeply self-centred man, had ever been known to make the slightest sacrifices for. His wit and his talent and his attractive appearance adequately saved him from oblivion and unnecessary hardships. There had been plenty of women in his life, but only one wife, and she had died too easily and without protest when Jaime was born.

Somehow, with the help of several faithful and unrewarded inamoratas, Jaime had been reared, though from that day forward Derrick Gilmore made no mention of his wife or of his wife's family, whom Jaime came to suspect he detested. It was almost like being an orphan, but her father in his own way adored her. By the time she was nineteen, she had almost forgotten she had a mother and somewhere, perhaps, a ready-made family. Now she stood in the scented shade of the massed oleanders, listening to the sound of voices. Her father's charming, light drawl filled with obvious bonhomie, and that of another in no sense gay, but dark and resonant, with a subtle glint of steel through the velvet. A voice that partly filled her with dread, because what he was saying was audible and he was talking about her.

All at once Jaime moved, running up the stairs, sliding back the glass door and entering the one large room in the house, the living-dining room. If it was attractively and imaginatively furnished, all due to her own efforts, she didn't notice as she whipped the sunglasses off the bridge of her nose.

'Jaime, love!' her father cried delightedly, a satisfied smile at her beauty, 'we didn't hear you!'

'I heard you!' she said abruptly, her glance locked with that of the stranger who had come to his feet, appraising her so absolutely. 'But I didn't understand the lines!'

Her father laughed again. 'My daughter is a wonderful girl, Mr Sterling, and clever too, though I expect you didn't miss that!'

'Among other things!' the stranger rejoined smoothly, responding to Derrick Gilmore's introductions and moving towards Jaime's instinctively outstretched hand. His marked attention was odd and rather frightening, but it was real and it almost defeated her. There was no hint of the immediate and often unwelcome admiration she had already become used to, but a glittering silent scrutiny she endured as long as possible. She might well have been a questionable collector's item, not a living girl, so dehumanising was that searching gaze.

She couldn't keep the tremble out of her hand and she had to look up a good way to him. 'How do you do, Mr Sterling.'

'Jaime.' He held her hand for an instant only, then released it. He was a man of an added dimension. The kind of man who drew recognition, a man who belonged to a world of power and position—an unfamiliar world. He was very tall and superbly lean, with hair as black as her own and brilliant black eyes to match. A ruthless adversary if you like, with those silver points of light at the centre of his eyes, the dark, high-bred features rather remote until he favoured her at long last with a smile. It ridded his sombre dark face of its formidable quality, revealing an exact and easy command of a brand of charm her father could never hope to aspire to for all his careful study and application of that very asset. Jaime felt almost crushed into insignificance beside him with her bare feet and her wet swimsuit and her damp trail of hair. The excuse to escape was a godsend.

'I'll go and change,' she said hurriedly, 'I seem to be dripping sea water all over the place.'

'No hurry, darling!' her father said brightly. 'Mr Sterling is staying on for a while. You'll share a meal with us, surely?' He turned to the younger man.

'If you're sure it's no bother,' Quinn Sterling answered conventionally but with no trace of diffidence in his disturbing voice.

'No bother at all, my dear fellow! Jaime is an excellent cook, aren't you, darling?'

'I'll allow Mr Sterling to discover that, as he's staying.' Distrust and hostility were in her voice and Quinn Sterling turned his dark head swiftly to acknowledge it. 'I'll be glad to give an opinion, Jaime,' he said with light mockery.

'Now what about a drink?' Derry Gilmore suggested in a tone full of lustre, but Jaime waited to hear no more. She flew along the passageway to her room, her skin crawling with a frightful awareness. She was unable to even consider what lay beyond this visit. What she had overheard and its significance alarmed her. She only knew her own world, yet Quinn Sterling was here to remove her from it, and all apparently with her father's approval when he had refused her plea to continue her art studies in the city and come home at the weekends. It didn't make sense, nor his bogus affability. She wasn't such a child that she couldn't detect acting on both sides.

A sick little feeling began to press down on her. She closed her door and locked it for God knows what reason, then stepped out of her things. The small room reflected the golden warmth of the afternoon, drying her body. She shook out her long hair and went to the built-in wardrobe, selecting, inexplicably, her prettiest after-sundown dress, one she had designed and made herself, hand-painting the ankle-length hemline with flowers and birds. It was easy to imagine she had paid quite a price for it, so professional was the concept and finish, but what to wear would never be too much of a problem to her, for she was unusually gifted at handling fabric, the design, cut-out and assembly. Irresistibly her mind was drawn back to Lucy, the nicest and kindest of all her father's women friends. Lucy, with her own small dressmaking business, had taught the young Jaime to sew, in turn delighted and surprised at her pupil's aptitude. At one time, Jaime had hoped her father would make an honest woman out of Lucy until he had told her quite plainly that Lucy under the same roof would drive him insane. That had been nearly nine years ago, but Jaime had never forgotten Lucy, nor her many kindnesses and interest in Jaime for her own sake. The rest of them had only been interested in her father. One day she would repay Lucy, but obviously not now when she was only a penniless nineteen-year-old with a few hidden talents. Well, not so hidden. A few people had provided her with a few sincere, straightforward compliments.

She had to use the hand dryer to finish off her hair, then she parted it in the centre and drew it back into a smooth shining chignon on her nape, leaving a few softening side and nape tendrils. Her mirrored face, wearing a little make-up, looked unfamiliar. She usually didn't bother except for a lip gloss to protect her mouth and no one could find fault with her skin. She mightn't look expensive, but she looked perfectly presentable.

She wasn't out to impress anyone anyway.

When she went back to the living room her father gave her a sly, conspiratorial grin as if she had spent her time attempting to do just that. Quinn Sterling came to his feet and she waved him down again.

'Please don't let me disturb you. I've been eavesdropping all my life. Here, let me get you something to go with that drink!'

'Then come and join us, darling!' her father said. 'Mr Sterling has something to tell you.'

'I can always listen from here. Just who are you, Mr Sterling?'

'Better wait until you're sitting down,' Derrick Gilmore suggested dryly, enjoying himself in some awful way.

Jaime shrugged again, aware that Quinn Sterling was watching her. She tipped olives into a bowl, found crackers and pretzels and cheese and got them all together in a beautiful polished wood platter with separate compartments. The men were drinking icy cold beer, so she poured herself a glass of red wine and walked down the two steps from the raised kitchen area into the living-dining room.

Quinn Sterling got up to take the platter from her and set it down on the long low occasional table her father had made with its beaten copper top. Jaime sank into the armchair opposite him, admiring the way he wore his clothes despite herself; the beautiful casual jacket and slacks, the body shirt he teamed with it. She would always have this eye for cut and line and she had to admit Quinn Sterling had a lot of things going for him. She tipped her head to one side, studying him.

'Well?'

He raised his eyes to her and she found herself flushing without even knowing why. 'I don't know how much you overheard, Jaime, but I've been sent here by your grandfather.'

Jaime reached out for her glass and took a sip because her mouth had gone so dry. 'My *mother's* father?'

'Your mother's father!' Derrick Gilmore confirmed, his hazel eyes crinkling against the spurt of cigarette smoke he sent up.

'Glory be to God!' said Jaime, in evidence of her four years at a convent school. 'I suppose you realise, Mr Sterling, I didn't even know I had a grandfather.'

'Oh, you have one, darling,' Derrick Gilmore said, undeniably malicious.

'The one you never told me about,' Jaime shot at him, irritated and full of suspense.

'The same one,' her father smiled unpleasantly. 'Look here, Sterling, why don't I let you tell your own story? I haven't a decent wine to offer you for dinner. I'll just slip down to the pub while you're talking.'

'There's the dry red you had no objection to last night,' Jaime pointed out, frowning.

'I think our guest deserves something much better than that, my darling. You're no judge as yet. Besides, he's come a long way.'

And I don't give a damn about that! Jaime thought, her eyes flashing.

'Please yourself,' Quinn Sterling said dryly, not taking either of them too seriously.

Derrick Gilmore got up immediately, a slight, very attractive man, still disgustingly boyish-looking in middle age with his bleached blond hair and smooth deeply-tanned skin. 'I won't be more than ten minutes,' he said, beginning the usual hunt for the car keys.

'They're in the pottery bowl, Derry,' Jaime said with faint outrage. 'The same place I always leave them.'

'Very methodical, my daughter. She doesn't take after her dear father in that respect. Right now!' he flourished the keys before them. 'Tell her the important news, Sterling. It might take a few minutes to penetrate, even allowing for the fact she's intelligent. I've kept her pretty much in the dark regarding the Borgias.'

'It's very kind of you to allow me,' Quinn Sterling said suavely.

'Think nothing of it!' Derrick went out quickly and after a minute they heard the car start up and pull away from the front of the house.

Jaime was not unduly upset at losing her father's support. He had been doing the same kind of thing for years and it had made her more than usually self-reliant. Anyway, she loved him and wasn't torn to change him. Quinn Sterling had settled back in his chair, his brilliant dark eyes taking in every aspect of Jaime's appearance, but whether he was pleased or not it was impossible to tell.

'The young Rowena,' he finally offered with perceptible irony.

'Oh yes, my mother! I've only one photograph of her. It isn't very good.'

'You have a mirror, haven't you?'

'So you knew my mother?' she asked eagerly.

'I saw her many times when I was a boy. Never after she married your father.'

'Derry wasn't good enough, I suppose?'

'Actually, Jaime,' he said rather impatiently, 'your mother was engaged to my Uncle Nigel. She left him quite literally at the altar where most of us would die of stupid pride. He was there. The church was packed. She wasn't—she'd run off to marry your father. Nigel never forgave her for that. Very few men would if they were given to high drama. Nigel was, and died poetic-

12

ally about six months after. But that's in the past.'

Jaime couldn't take it calmly. 'I'm sorry,' she said, gripping her glass. 'It seems unbelievable!'

'I assure you it's quite true. I can see that it has affected you, but it's exactly the way it happened. You've heard of Hunter Sterling, I suppose?'

'The consulting engineers, freeways, bridges, all that sort of thing?'

'Rolf Hunter is your grandfather. Sir Rolf Hunter. He was knighted a few years back.'

'Not for his humanity, I'm sure!' she snapped.

'Hard to take, Jaime?' he asked rather curtly. 'Your mother was Rowena Hunter.' Up until now the most beautiful woman I've ever seen, he thought dispassionately, but didn't consider mentioning it. Rowena Hunter had had that same true, rare shade of black hair, the same exquisite Oriental blue eyes, the same arching black brows, and neat, elegant bones, all of which was making him angry, yet Jaime, the daughter, had a vibrant, challenging quality that Rowena Hunter's painted face at least had lacked. Very likely, she would inspire the same sort of spineless passion. Putting a woman on a pedestal had definite disadvantages. In a way it was priceless, poor old Nigel's romance; the old horror story in the family. He longed all of a sudden to hurt this child, then immediately was irritated most of all by himself. The whole thing was fantastic, yet he was here to take her captive. The Old Man would stop at nothing to have his granddaughter returned to him. She had her head tilted back for a moment, her eyes closed, the lovely line of her throat and chin unconsciously provocative. She couldn't help it, this pure sensuality, it clung to her like a second skin.

'So I resemble my mother,' she was saying in a hushed voice.

'Almost exactly. The colouring certainly, the bone structure. Hers was an unusual beauty far more dangerous than prettiness. Your grandfather adored her. She was his only daughter. He was fond of my Uncle Nigel as well, in fact he promoted the match—one of his few mistakes. Sir Rolf and my grandfather founded the Hunter Sterling Corporation—nearly all of us in both families have gone into the firm. You have uncles and cousins you've never even heard about.'

'I've no room in my heart to love them,' she pointed out dryly. 'They mean nothing to me. I might have been nuts about them had they dandled me on their knees. But why should my grandfather send you to me, Mr Sterling? Why should he suddenly bother now? I mean, I've never meant a thing to him for nearly twenty years.'

'You can believe that, but it's not true. Anyway, I won't attempt to explain that part of it to you. I think the whole thing is a mistake. Your mother had everything, wealth, beauty, position, a fiancé who became too unhappy and morose to live without her. She threw it all up for your father. Had she lived, who knows, your grandfather might have been moved to heal the great rift in the family, but she died when you were born—tragedy all round. In fairness to Sir Rolf your father did his level best to outrage and wound everyone at the funeral. Apparently he did it to perfection, further isolating the old man.'

'Surely his grief allowed him a few hasty words? I asked you before and you didn't answer me, why *now*?'

Quinn Sterling shrugged. 'Human nature, perhaps. He's old now and the things that once were important to him no longer seem to matter. He wants to see you, make amends. You're not his only granddaughter. Your mother had two brothers and they have daughters a few years older than you are, but it's you he wants to see.'

'The outsider?'

His autocratic dark face suggested he agreed with her. 'Something like that, Jaime, and you never knew your grandfather's identity?'

'Would I say I didn't if I did?'

'Please tell me.'

'I've told you, Mr Sterling. My father has never breathed a word either about my mother or her entire family. I might have come out of a cabbage. I've heard of Hunter Sterling, of course, who hasn't? They're practically a household word in this country. But why send you? You're not a member of my family. Why not one of my uncles or my cousins? I might have had something in common with them.'

'I could have been your cousin, Jaime, perish the thought. As it happens your grandfather trusts me to handle a lot of his affairs quite outside Corporation matters. I had to come to Queensland on business in any case. It's been a little difficult to track you down. You've lived in so many places.'

'Dragged up, why don't you say it?' she flared.

'Possibly because I never thought it,' he said tersely, looking as though he'd like to turn her over his knee.

She stared back at him unrepentant, her dark blue eyes hazed with violet. 'I suppose I should be overcome and burst into floods of grateful tears, but the fact is I don't want to. I might have needed my grandfather once, but I don't any more.'

'Must I underline the fact he hasn't long to live?'

'How old is he anyway? Late sixties, early seventies?'

'He's seventy-two and he survived a massive heart attack last year. He won't again. Aren't you curious,

15

Jaime, even if you're determined not to be compassionate?'

Her heart seemed to twist and she hated him for his consummate ability to place her in the wrong. 'You come to me, a stranger,' she said a little wildly, 'talking about either?'

'I'm not a stranger at all,' he pointed out. 'I've been used to your face since I was a small boy. There's a portrait of your mother in the drawing room at Falconer, your grandfather's home.'

'I'm surprised it wasn't removed!', she flashed at him.

'It was for some years.'

'I wish I had it, I would treasure it,' she said impulsively.

Through the black glimmering lashes he saw the startling blue eyes ablaze with sudden tears. Her eyes were remarkable, Ming blue into mauve, the same beautiful underglaze blue he had seen in Imperial Chinese porcelain. She was an exotic young creature and once her grandfather had her, he would guard her fiercely. It was his intention anyway, that much Quinn knew.

Only the fact that his own taste didn't include young girls permitted him to sit back and study her so dispassionately. Her dress was a soft yet dense blue several shades lighter than her eyes, and it had to be a prized possession, for it was beautifully cut and designed, hand-painted in the Oriental fashion with birds and flowering sprays of blossom in pinks and jade and bluish purple. Despite her youth, she wore it with considerable panache, her flawless young skin gleaming against the duller sheen of the fabric.

Instead of being the forlorn orphan, she would hopelessly outshine her cousins, not that they weren't angry

16

enough and shocked into bewilderment by the Old Man's decision to invite Rowena's daughter to Falconer. Only she was so beautiful and in complete contrast to what he had expected; he would have felt sorry for her, but she was a fighter, a confident young creature, not lost and lovely. There was a delicate determination and strength to those precisely cut features, shown to great advantage with her hair swept severely back to her nape. He hadn't the slightest doubt she would stir up a lot of feeling with her flame-like quality. No one, not even Rolf, would crush her if his assessment of her temperament was accurate. Perhaps she had a lot of the Old Man in her.

Something about his expression, a dark brooding, made the colour burn in her cheeks. 'What are you thinking about?' she demanded.

'If I told you, Jaime, I'd regret it.'

'I can't imagine my uncles and cousins would be pleased to see me,' she said.

'Only your Uncle Gerard lives at Falconer with his father. His wife's name is Georgina and they have a son and daughter, Simon and Sue-Ellen, both of them several years older than you are.'

A faint tension was on him, showing itself in the set of his midnight-dark head, the hard, charming smile.

'How did your uncle die?' she asked him.

'By design,' he said in a voice that completely stopped her, and she blurted:

'I can't see you suffering on a woman's account.'

'You're dead right!'

'You don't like me, do you?'

'If I'm bound to answer you, I don't have to like you, Jaime, nor you me. It's not important. The thing for you to do is consider your grandfather's invitation.'

'Have no fear, I will. What *is* it exactly?'

He leaned forward, not taking his eyes off her. 'Come to Falconer for an indefinite period. As long as you like. An extended holiday if you like.'

'And what am I supposed to do all day?'

'I'm sure that'll be no problem.'

'What do my cousins do?'

'Simon has a degree in law. He's part of the firm, the Hunter Sterling Land Corporation. Sue-Ellen keeps busy pulling out all the pleasure stops.'

'That's all very well, but I have to earn my living.'

'What do you do now?' he asked.

'Look after my father.'

'Surely he can look after himself?' He lifted one eyebrow.

'I mean I assist him with his work, the painting and the pottery—the donkey work, of course, but I have ability of my own. I wanted to do a fine arts course, but I couldn't talk him into it.'

'Couldn't you do it yourself?'

'Courses have to be paid for, Mr Sterling.'

He gave her a mocking, speculative look. 'Then I think you should be pretty happy to accept your grandfather's invitation. Now that I've seen you, I think he'll give you anything you want in this world.'

'He can't give me my mother back or all the lost years.'

'Were they lonely?'

His brilliant black eyes seemed to be raying right through her and she averted her head, her heart beating rapidly. 'Of course they were. What a question! I don't think you're trying to persuade me overmuch.'

'True. I think you'll make up your own mind.'

She turned her head back quickly to meet those veiled dark eyes. 'Or you have a very subtle way of

18

manipulating people, Mr Sterling. What's your position in the scheme of things?'

'Aide to the General,' he said, his eyes gleaming.

'What about my uncles and cousins?'

'They're around.'

'It's strange, nevertheless, that you were chosen. What were you looking for, the supreme opportunist?'

'I was looking for Rowena's daughter.'

'A rare honour due to my grandfather's advanced age and mellowness. Well, your trip didn't work out as well as you thought, because I don't feel like visiting Falconer at this late stage, and I don't feel like meeting the lions.'

'You ought to. You aren't the one to curl up quietly in a corner.'

'I mean to shine in my own way, Mr Sterling,' she retorted.

'Can't you make it Quinn? After all, I've been calling you Jaime.'

'And I didn't say you could!'

'You're not serious!' His glance travelled over her.

'Perhaps you thought you were jollying along a schoolgirl?'

'I know exactly how old you are, Jaime. I even know your birthday.'

'Go on, what else?'

'That you're stubborn.'

'Moderately. Surely you didn't expect me to act the dutiful, loving granddaughter—let bygones be bygones!'

'As a matter of fact I do. Your grandfather is a very rich man. I think he wants to put his affairs in order. Not the business, that's all taken care of, but family matters. You may think it extremely odd, but he adored

19

your mother, and he's notably anxious to transfer that adoration to you.'

'How charming!' She flickered him a burningly blue glance. 'There's no denying a miracle has occurred to soften his old heart.'

'They do happen.'

'I suppose I should be generous,' she pondered.

'Don't imagine him a suffering silver-haired old gentleman,' he said. 'Your grandfather's formidability is enormous.'

'Do you like him?' she asked with concentrated attention.

'I admire him in many ways. He's brilliant and shrewd and ruthless and his business faculty is little short of genius.'

'In other words, someone like you.'

'Do I seem that way to you, Jaime?'

'Yes, or you're planning to be!'

'Will you come?' he asked.

He had a fascinating voice that could shrivel a woman under different circumstances, she thought. 'I wonder if my mother would want me to? Did you hate my mother, by the way, for what she did to your uncle?'

'I was only a boy,' he said, looking at her through hooded lids.

'Children feel and erupt. I think you're fairly volcanic under that patrician remoteness.'

'If you were a woman you might find out, but you're only an impudent child.'

'Oh no, I'm not!' she said softly, knowing he was not to be trusted, but against her will liking the sound and the sight of him. 'Anyway,' she said, pretending a casualness she did not feel, 'I'll have to speak to Derry.'

'He's all for it!'

'I gathered as much, but what I don't know is *why*?'

Something flickered in his night-black eyes, an intolerable cynicism. 'Perhaps your father has decided your mother's portion is due to you and you'd better go along and collect it.'

'One powerful reason not to go at all!' she said passionately.

'Do you fear a family reaction—jealousy?'

'In a word, *no*! I don't fear one of those Christian souls. Not only did my grandfather desert me but my uncles as well. They're all pretty short on charity. What about the Sterlings? They must have known my mother well?'

'I believe they treated her like a daughter, but their love and trust was shattered when she eloped with your father. Nigel's habitual stupor, then untimely demise, eventually and understandably hardened their hearts.'

'Why did she do it?' she murmured, staring at him with her glowing blue eyes.

'That's a strange question from you, Jaime. Obviously she was quite mad about your father. He's taken good care of you, hasn't he?'

'I've no complaints!' And forget the bad times, she thought.

He was silent for a minute, his dark gaze holding her still. 'Family ties bind us all. Come to Falconer and meet your grandfather.'

'And leave in an hour if I decide to?' she insisted.

'I'll drive you to the airport myself.'

'I might keep you to that, Mr Sterling.'

'That sounds as if you're coming.'

'I might take an instant dislike to him.'

'As you've taken to me?'

She caught the mockery on his face and the brilliance of his gaze dazzled her. 'I don't dislike you, Mr Sterling,' she said with mock gentleness, 'I just don't trust

21

you, that's all. Neither should my grandfather.'

'Now why on earth should you say that?'

'There's a lot goes on behind your black eyes.'

He smiled and leaned forward, catching her hand in his lean strong fingers. 'I'll try not to keep anything from *you*, Jaime, if you come. And please do call me Quinn.'

'I might, but deep inside me I'll think of you as a Sterling, maybe even the enemy.'

'The reverse is true,' he said, pinning her trembling wrist. 'I'll never hurt you.'

'You've wanted to at least once since we've met.'

'Do you really think so?'

He released her and her hand fell away. 'Men like you sometimes do feel like that.'

'You'd better tell me what you mean, Jaime. You look very sheltered to me for all your bravado.'

'I don't mean anyone *has* ever hurt me, I mean I can recognise male hostility.'

'I could appreciate it better if you'd only sensed interest,' he rejoined.

'That too.'

'Well, you should be a meek little girl with sandy hair instead of a challenging beauty.'

'That doesn't mean you can't be kind to me,' she said.

'Does it matter anyway, Jaime?'

'No, but having you on my side would be a help rather than a hindrance.'

'You're so right!'

She got up and turned on a light and it splashed down on her shining jet black hair. She was a lovely, destructive young thing, perhaps already set on her mother's path, promising all the lure of the Garden of Eden and delivering nothing. Rowena the witch had made a battlefield of his family, and made a few people

22

desperately unhappy. What was he doing here helping her daughter to put some other poor fool in bondage? Her beauty at that moment was almost an affront and it was unstressed, unpolished and still heart-stopping. She might start off an epidemic of self-executions. Quinn nearly groaned aloud as so many memories passed before his eyes in a pitiless kaleidoscope. His white teeth clamped together and he looked towards the paintings on the wall, deliberately seeking out a safe topic.

'Do you paint yourself?'

'A little,' she said, aware of the menace in him.

'Do you get paid for it?'

'No.'

'What would you like to do?' he asked rather curtly. Besides go to a man's head, he thought to himself ironically.

There was about him a palpable aura of sexual antagonism against which Jaime had to protect herself. He might say he didn't resent her, but he did. Perhaps he didn't see her as herself at all but a girl in a portrait. He realised she hadn't answered him and he turned his head to her.

'I said what would you like to do?'

'I heard you.' Her blue-violet eyes met his directly and quite fearlessly. 'Something creative, I think. I have potential.'

'That you have, but in what field were you thinking of?'

'Women's fashions perhaps. I think I'd like to start my own business—design, cut-out assembly. I can handle the lot.'

'Did you make that dress you have on?'

'I did,' she said with not a flicker of self-consciousness.

'Then you obviously know what you're about, but it takes a lot more than that.'

'I'm aware of it, and I'm not about to ask my grandfather to pitch in and help.'

'Let it lie for a moment, Jaime. Who taught you to sew?'

'A good friend a long time ago,' she said almost aggressively, 'a few years at school. It's a natural flair and easy enough. I learnt it all in a quarter of the time, though the nuns were very good teachers. The only mistake they made was in thinking all girls sew well naturally. They don't.'

'I believe it. Your cousins Sue-Ellen and Leigh have never plied a needle in their lives.'

'How do you know?'

'I know them quite well. In any case I've never seen them look better than you do in that dress.'

'There's nothing wrong with your flattery,' she said definitely.

'Why pretend?' He lifted his head and stared at her. 'You know how you look.'

She sighed at the hardness of his expression. 'Which mightn't make my cousins so fond of me.'

'Perhaps not. We'll exclude Simon and Brett.'

Jaime frowned. 'It's difficult to keep track of all the names. I don't really think it would work. I can see by your face you can't assure me of a warm welcome.'

'That's overdoing it!' he said as though he meant it. 'I thought you told me you were moderate.'

'I'm not really.'

'I know that. One good reason why I think you'll come.'

'Do you always know how people will react?' she asked.

24

'I've had considerable experience. Isn't it true you like to hurdle difficulties?'

'I usually shove myself over them. If you're going to stay and have dinner with us, I'd better prepare it.'

'Why don't I take you out to a restaurant? Your father won't mind.'

'Well, that's a suggestion,' she said, looking at him in surprise. 'I sometimes feel sorry for myself.'

'You're not honour bound to cook for your father all the time. He's still a young man and he did mention a particular friend. Tavia, isn't it?'

'He'll never marry her,' Jaime said briefly.

'Why not?'

'I'm sure of it,' she said rather tautly. 'The flesh is weak but the head is strong.'

He laughed under his breath, a dark attractive sound. 'There's always the woman to upset a man's plans.'

'I didn't ask you, are you married?'

For the first time she looked little more than a child, an honest question in her dark blue eyes. 'Don't look so earnest, Jaime,' he taunted her. 'I'm not a bad man asking you out to dinner and then a stroll on a moonlit beach. I'm a determined bachelor.'

'I can almost hear the Thank God!'

'Don't tell me!' His black eyes mocked her.

'To my certain knowledge you thought it.'

'So I did. I might have known with your black hair and your blue eyes you'd be a witch. That's what poor old Nigel used to call your mother. Rowena, the witch!'

'Who brought him to grief.'

'She didn't fare so well herself.'

'God knows that's true.'

'Now what?' he asked rather tersely.

'Don't confuse me with my mother.'

'It's difficult not to. I know every line of your face,

the shape of your eyes and the tilt of your brows, even the curve of your cheek. Only the expression is different. You'll see what I mean when you get to Falconer.'

Jaime shook her head a little as though he was trying to put her into a trance. 'I don't need to bother with anyone else's face, not even my mother's. Anyway, Derry painted my portrait not so long ago. Would you like to see it? It might rid you of the vision of the other one—the one you don't like.'

'You're determined to read my mind, Jaime.'

'I would say I'm not too far off now. Do you want to see the portrait?'

'I can't think of anything I'd like better at the moment.'

'I'd get it, but it's too heavy to move and I'd have to stand on a chair. You'll have to come to it. It's in my room.'

Her heart was racing and she stood up, determined to hold fast on the giddy feeling that had befallen her since she met this man.

'You lead and I'll follow,' he said with a faint smile. 'What's the matter, Jaime, you did invite me.'

'There's nothing the matter,' she said abruptly, 'and I wouldn't admit it even if there were!'

'Good girl! I couldn't have taught you better myself.'

'I thought that myself,' she admitted. 'It's best to size up the other side should our lives get linked up.'

Something flickered in his black eyes. 'You're going to make your mark, Jaime!'

'I have a few projects in mind. Most of my father's women friends have been women on their own—women who've had to turn their hands to something to support themselves and their children of broken marriages. No man is going to have me at his mercy. Whatever assets I've got I'm going to use them to their fullest extent. I'm always going to be ready.'

'You might make some men nervous, Jaime.'

'Not you, I'm sure!'

'I was brought up in a hard school myself. Incidentally, it was all to the good, though I often wanted to alter it at the time.'

'You look unassailable now,' she commented.

'Is that a compliment, Jaime? It doesn't sound like it.'

'It's a compliment in its way, coupled with something else I'll leave you to find out.'

'That's guaranteed to keep me on a knife edge.' He moved a little closer to her and the room seemed to spin. It was a strange feeling and she was a stranger to it. He was looking at her intently, his head tipped to one side. Probably it was the difference in their ages. She was nineteen, almost twenty. He had to be thirty-four or five, a successful, sophisticated man with a frightening attraction for her beneath the unvarnished distrust. She moved quickly and a little jerkily as if she were in a cage. 'Let's see if my portrait holds up, shall we?'

He followed her out of the room and along the passageway, looking idly around him, liking what he saw. The bedroom door was open and Jaime switched on the light and walked to the centre of the room with Quinn Sterling coming to stand close behind her shoulder. The portrait, oil on canvas, about four feet by three, hung directly above the old Victorian brass bed with its tailored spread in a bright modern print. So naturally was Jaime posed against a blue sky, so exact her image, that one could hardly take one's eyes off her in case she came down from the plain gilded frame. It

27

was unquestionably Derrick Gilmore's best work and he was the first to admit it. It was indisputably Jaime, the character and the strength and the purpose alongside the beauty and delicate sensitivity. The raven hair gleamed and the beautiful violet eyes were clear and smiling.

'What do you think?' Jaime asked lightly, feeling quite differently about her painted image.

'She makes me feel slightly uncomfortable,' he said, his head back and his eyes narrowed.

'Why?' Jaime asked in surprise.

'Perhaps I feel I know her too well and I don't know her at all.'

'Do you like her?'

'Liking is irrelevant. It's extremely good. It has to be your father's best work.'

'Surely you haven't seen enough to judge?'

'On the contrary, I've seen quite a bit,' he muttered, lowering his head to glance at her. 'I visited the gallery before I came here.'

'Typical, I suppose.'

'It's just a question of researching a job.' He frowned and looked back at the portrait. 'Your grandfather would like this.'

'It's not for sale,' she said instantly.

'I'm not suggesting you sell it, Jaime, but *give* it.'

'A nice gesture, but I'm not considering making it.'

'Then I won't press it, but it would rate instant approval.'

She was uneasy and on edge, struck into incredulity by the antagonism and attraction this man stirred up. It was strange and it made her angry, but she was always honest with herself. This tenseness and excitement she was feeling all stemmed from Quinn Sterling, and his presence so close beside her offered no respite. She moved away from him towards the door, her dark blue eyes startling against her golden tan. 'Approval is pleasant,' she remarked crisply, 'but buying it, isn't my style. It's not necessary for the Hunters or Sterlings to like me. I can only think of you as "those people" anyway.'

Quinn took one last look at the painting, his chiselled mouth faintly ironic. 'You'll remind them all a great deal of your mother.'

'Of whom they haven't had a recent thought for the past twenty years.'

'Don't be bitter, Jaime. Considering they all toe your grandfather's line that's not surprising.'

'Do you?' she asked, her violet eyes gleaming with speculation.

'We're all one big, happy family!' He joined her at the door, looking down at her, almost holding her immobile. –

She shook her head and freed herself. 'Nice work if you can make them believe it. I think you have your own private axe to grind.'

'Surely you're a witch, Jaime!' His black eyes mocked her, but there was a glimmer of surprise somewhere there as well.

'I wouldn't care to cross you myself,' she replied.

'I'm glad!' he said silkily, 'because you'll be seeing quite a lot of me.'

'Tell me about the business,' she asked.

'It's big and it's complex. It would take a long time.'

'I shouldn't be in ignorance of it.'

'I think, Jaime, you've changed your mind,' he teased.

'Maybe I'm like you, Mr Sterling, with my own axe to grind.'

'You'll make yourself unhappy doing it!' Unexpectedly he caught her shoulder and turned her towards him. 'Listen to me, Jaime, you're beautiful and you're clever, but you wouldn't last the first round with them because you couldn't fight their way.'

She stared up at him fixedly. 'What is Hunter Sterling, a battlefield?'

'All big business is intrigue, Jaime.'

'I'm not interested in the business and I've learned how to defend myself.'

'Then I fail to understand why you're trembling under my hands.'

'That doesn't mean all that much.'

'As it happens it might, only I don't care to have a young girl at my mercy.'

'Then you've got the wrong impression. To begin with, I don't *like* you.'

'I damn well don't believe it!' He released her with his rare, very attractive smile.

Her glance flicked back over him and she was talking fast. 'You're at liberty to doubt it. I don't know why or how, but my opinion is formed!'

'You're not very careful with your insults, Jaime.'

'It's you who's asking the favour of me.'

He held up his hand. '*Please!* I think it's a mistake your coming to Falconer. It's your grandfather who wants you.'

'Presumably you haven't suffered by making this visit. I mean, aren't all your expenses paid?'

'It would be a very unpleasant surprise to discover they haven't. That includes the dinner.'

'Thank you for telling me. Suddenly I don't feel hungry.'

'You will!' he promised.

She shrugged her delicate shoulders. 'I don't really need any little pats on the head.'

'No, what you really need is a few hard slaps some place else.'

She felt suddenly like laughing and did. 'What did I tell you? Already we're running short on civility.' She stepped back and looked out through the window. 'Mercifully Derry's coming back, and there's someone with him. Oh God, it's Tavia.'

'Then let's go out.'

She turned her head back to stare at him, so fantastically sure of himself. 'I've tried and tried to like Tavia—she works in the gallery.'

'I know.'

'Do you know everything?' she asked.

'All the important information. Make up your mind, Jaime, I'll rescue you if you want me too.'

'I've no alternative now Tavia's arrived.'

'Your father's a big boy.'

'Is he?' she asked, making no attempt to smile. 'I promised myself I would look after him for as long as I could.'

'Then now's the time to get out.'

'I daresay it would suit your plans—oh, forgive me, my *grandfather's* plans.'

'I'm only the errand boy,' he said, his brilliant eyes gleaming.

She watched him across the room. 'Oh no, you're not,' she said softly, 'you're a real Machiavelli!'

'I'm no threat to little girls.'

'Hush, they're coming.'

Quinn smiled. 'What are we, Jaime, unwilling conspirators?'

'It looks like it, doesn't it? You've got me, finally. We'll go out.'

With the length of the room separating them, their eyes met and held. He found himself becoming more

31

and more involved with this vital young creature. She couldn't have offered a more complete contrast to her cousins; for all her perceptible integrity and courage a babe in the woods beside either of them, Sue-Ellen or Leigh. They heard the car engine cut, then a moment later Derrick Gilmore let himself in the front door accompanied by a rather voluptuous-looking redhead in her late thirties.

'Hello there!' Derrick said with a challenging smile. 'Sorry I was so long, but I ran into Tavvy, here.'

'Nice to see you again, Mr Sterling,' Tavia said in her fruity contralto. 'Hi there, Jaime. That's a terrific outfit as usual. I wish you'd make something for me. I have to pay the earth!'

'When I come to it I might charge the earth!' Jaime answered rather shortly. 'There's been a change in plan, Derry. Mr Sterling is taking me out to dinner.'

'What a good idea!' said Tavia, obviously taken with Quinn Sterling. 'Can't we all go? The Plantation is fabulous and it's new.'

'It seems to me you weren't invited!' Jaime burst out, irritated by the way Tavia had transferred her whole attention to Quinn Sterling.

'I perfectly agree,' said her father. 'We'll have a nice dinner at home, Tavvy, and polish off this bottle of wine.'

'Why?' Tavia turned her almond amber eyes on him.

'Because we do most of the time.'

'I'll certainly grant you that!' Tavia said, looking at Jaime with veiled dislike. 'Naturally it's none of my business, but have you decided to visit your grandfather?'

'From which I gather Derry has been gossiping again?'

'Why not?' asked Tavia, her eyes sliding back to

Quinn Sterling's tall, lean figure. He was assuredly the sexiest man she had ever seen. Derry at his best couldn't come remotely close, though he was far more attractive than any other man in her circle. This man was something else again, with his lean rather imperious face and his coal-black eyes. Behind the charm, and he had it far more dangerously, than Derry, there was a high degree of ruthlessness. No woman could afford to underestimate him for a second. A pity to waste him on a fledgling like Jaime.

'I'll let you know early,' Jaime assured her.

'It seems to me we're holding you up,' Derry said affably, the expression in his hazel eyes not matching up. 'Enjoy yourselves. I'll still be up by the time you get home.'

'Which reminds me,' Quinn Sterling looked back at the older man, 'your portrait of Jaime is excellent.'

'Not too bad at all!' Derrick agreed contentedly. 'She's the kind of model most artists dream about.'

'There's a portrait of Rowena at Falconer.'

'I never saw it. Is it surrounded by flowers and candles like a shrine?'

Jaime shuddered. 'Don't speak like that, Derry!'

'I was amusing myself. I hope that old swine has suffered and suffered!'

'He has no less than you have!' Quinn Sterling said in his black velvet voice with the steel in it.

'You couldn't *like* him!' Derry maintained, an odd whiteness about his mouth and nostrils. 'He's a past master of every dirty trick in the business. Didn't he practically force your father to resign?'

'He's not that good that we haven't always been able to come up with a counter-move.'

'From the look of you, you know how to survive!' Derry said grimly. 'Do you wonder I have no sort of ambition? I'd never have held Rowena, had she lived. She was used to a high level of living. A frightening old eagle for a father.'

'Yet you're willing to allow your daughter to visit him,' Quinn countered with no trace of pity or compassion on his dark face.

'Oh well!' Derry said, brightening, a puckish smile on his face, 'I'm sending her for her own sake. The old devil is a multi-millionaire. I think he should extend a few hundred thousand in Jaime's direction!'

'That's good! In your direction, you mean!' Tavia laughed cruelly.

'Take care, Tavvy, or you can walk home,' Derry warned.

'That would well-nigh kill me, I'm right out of condition.'

'A real Rubens!' Derry grinned, restored to good humour by the thought of her.

Jaime realised she was trembling. She had never really known her father; she only knew she had never felt carefree.

'Are you ready, Jaime?' Quinn asked, his eyes on her still face.

'Yes. I'll just get a stole, the breeze off the ocean is very cooling. I won't be a moment.' She hurried out of the room hearing Tavia beginning to question Quinn on his intended movements within the next few days. Probably if she could she would track him down. Tavia was a lady vulture, but at least Derry would never be her victim. Derry, she was now coming to suspect, didn't really need anyone beyond someone to attend to his creature comforts. Tavia might stay around him a long time, but he would never marry her. Derry totally rejected commitment, though in fairness had never forsaken his only child.

Whatever he was, Jaime loved him, though she thought of him as only a few years older than she was, so many scrapes had she got him out of. Tavia was lucky he wouldn't marry her. Damned lucky. Had he loved her mother when he had run away with her, or had he deliberately set out to spite and outrage an establishment that had refused to accept him? It sounded like Derry. He pitchforked himself into trouble. With a kind of nervous horror Jaime considered that he might be burning for vengeance, using her as once he had used her mother. No, it couldn't be so. He had loved Rowena and he had proved his love by never deserting Rowena's child. She couldn't allow these mysterious, repelling thoughts to race around in her head. Derry wouldn't use her as a form of blackmail over her grandfather. It was just a fantastic thought.

CHAPTER TWO

A LITTLE silence had fallen between them, and Quinn studied the young downbent face opposite him. Her skin in the soft rosy lighting had a wonderful sensuous quality, her dark blue eyes blurred with violet, yet suddenly she looked like a spent child.

'I think you're right, Jaime,' he offered with grave amusement. 'You have lost your appetite.'

'I've nothing to celebrate,' she said, twirling her wine glass, 'but please finish your lobster. This place is becoming famous for its seafood.'

'A deserved reputation, but you've hardly touched anything.'

'I feel rootless all of a sudden,' she looked up swiftly and directly into his night-dark eyes.

'How's that?'

'Oh, Derry seems anxious to get rid of me for one reason or the other.'

'Not get rid of you, Jaime. He feels quite rightly that your grandfather should acknowledge you at last and further provide for you in his will.'

'May he live on for ever!' she said fervently, and took a sip of her wine. 'I don't give a tinker's curse for his money.'

'Then you're the only member of his family who doesn't.'

'But don't you see,' she said earnestly, 'I'm not a member of the family. I'm Orphan Annie.'

'Anyone less like Orphan Annie I've yet to see,' he said dryly, reaching forward and filling up her wine glass.

'Tell me then, what is this marvellous gift he's offering me? The chance to bask in his reflected glory and get financially rewarded at the same time. With just a little help, I can make it on my own.'

'I wish you'd stop talking like a gallant child, and I'm beginning to think that's all you are. If you don't come, you'll end up getting nothing at all.'

Jaime lowered her face, immeasurably disenchanted. 'The one thing that would have redeemed my grandfather in my eyes would have been for him to remember me without even having laid eyes on me. There are strings attached to his benevolence.'

'Without a doubt,' he agreed.

'He wants me to console him in his old age, absolve him from his share of the blame or whatever.'

'He genuinely wants to love you.'

'What a beautiful thought!' she said, gazing straight at him. 'The first he's extended to me in all my young life.'

Despite himself he laughed, and the light fell across his dark profile. There was a glitter of sardonic amusement in his unfathomable eyes and the words seemed to bubble up in Jaime's throat. 'Just one thing, Quinn. You're not attempting at all to be reassuring.'

'You want me to tell you the truth, don't you?' he countered.

'I'm not so blind I can't see it for myself. My grandfather wants me to provide him with his salvation. Having been an enormous success in this life he naturally wants to make an unforgettable mark in the next.'

'I think he will,' he said suavely.

Her eyes were fastened on him with barely concealed apprehension. 'There's too much about you to fathom. I think you want to take over where my grandfather leaves off.'

'The idea appeals to me, Jaime.'

'What would you do with all my uncles and cousins?'

'Step over them.'

'How intolerable!'

'For them, yes,' he said blandly.

'I suppose they're blissfully unaware of your plans.'

'They'd demolish me if they could. Are you going to join them?'

'Not now. Not ever!' she said with quiet emphasis.

'Why not?'

'You'd make a dangerous enemy.'

'I'm harmless to my friends. Life had hardened me, Jaime. My grandfather was a brilliant but very trusting man, so was my father, but I have a few accounts to settle. Both of them were used, but I don't intend that anyone will use me.' A kind of lightning flashed out of his eyes and Jaime shivered, clasped her hands together and held them beneath her chin.

'You hate them, don't you?'

He smiled and the humour came back into his face. 'I don't have to, Jaime. My family holds forty-eight per cent of company stock. It didn't happen overnight and they didn't like it, but it happened. My family had the engineering brains, your grandfather was the financial genius. The Hunter Sterling Oil Exploration Company was my father's brainchild. It's only fair that we should now own fifty-one per cent of the stock in that company. I was able to persuade a few of our major shareholders to sell out to us; it set us right back for a time, but we're making up for that. Both my mother and father died within a few years of each other. My grandmother is head of the family.'

'Nigel's mother?'

He looked at her with brilliant, harsh alertness. 'Yes.'

'Then I could only cause her painful memories.'

'Infinitely painful, Jaime.'

'You're cruel,' she said softly, feeling tears threatening.

'And you, of course, can't be blamed for your astonishing resemblance to your mother. We'll have to keep remembering that. Your face will repay itself when your grandfather sees you.'

'I don't think I can take it all in! This morning none of this seemed imminent. That somewhere I had a grandfather, an important and powerful man. I remember reading once in the newspaper that some politician called him a megolomaniac.'

'With some reason, but that's the way giants are.'

'And he trusts you?'

'He knows I won't stoop to anything too low. That's the Sterling in me. A lot of people meeting me for the first time assume I'm a Hunter.'

'Well, is that bad?'

'Being a Sterling is a lot better,' he smiled.

'I guess I'll know when I meet them.'

'Both Simon and Brett will try to rush you into an early marriage,' he warned her.

'They're my cousins!'

'Cousins marry. Different mothers helps, if you want to look at it that way.'

Jaime shook her head. 'I'm like you—what I've seen of marriage, or rather broken marriages, worries me. I like men, I can't pretend not to, but I think they're very selfish, the best of them.'

'Keep going. You won't embarrass me.'

'All right! If you won't take any notice of my conversation, let's dance!' She stopped and looked at him, then retracted. 'No, on second thoughts we won't.'

'What angle are you working on now?'

'I've never met a man with such a suspicious mind. I've just reconsidered, that's all.'

'And what influenced you?'

'Your enormous charisma. This way I'll keep my feet on the ground.'

'Jaime?' He stood up and came round to her, slipping her chair back.

'It sounds as if you've made up *your* mind.'

'You're a grown woman, or almost, you don't have to dither. I don't like indecision.'

'That lets me off the hook, Mr Sterling. I'm very decisive, just wary about you.'

He smiled at her and led her out on to the dance floor where several other couples were involved with doing their own thing and came together only briefly; the rest in conventional positions enjoyed themselves just as much, but occupied the perimeter of the floor.

From the minute Quinn's arms closed around her Jaime knew she had shown wisdom in not underestimating him or his effect on her, but it was a matter of principle to look up at him and smile. She would make sure she never found herself in this position again.

'Stop frowning!' he said, and she was half mesmerised by the sound of his voice.

'Am I?'

'Yes. *And* thinking out loud. I'm the big bad wolf, that's plain, and it's quite undeserved. I've told you before, little girls don't awaken my interest.'

'I sincerely hope not.'

'Relax, Jaime!'

'I'd have to force myself to. The whole thing's crazy!'

'Surely it's better than staying home?'

'In a word, yes. Tavia doesn't value my company, or any woman's for that matter. She was even beginning to look at you.'

'Really? Then why aren't you smiling?'

'Not that it would have thrown Derry,' she pursued, 'he always bounces right back. It's Derry who's the bad bet, not Tavia. She would marry him tomorrow, impoverished artist and all.'

'Don't take it so seriously, Jaime. Your father can handle his own life.'

'What you mean is, I should start leading a life of my own.'

'It's quite possible you'll make quite a success of it.'

'Don't patronise me, Quinn Sterling!'

He nodded. 'All right. Anything else?'

'Tell me about my cousins.'

'I might as well. You might have reason to be grateful to me.'

Her glance lifted and she studied his dark face. 'If they're as bad as that, I'd better stay away.'

'You wanted my honest opinion,' he said lightly.

'Unbiased, I hope?'

'I can only try, Jaime. Your cousins, like your uncles and their wives, are controlled by your grandfather.'

'That's all?'

'Isn't that enough?'

'Who controls you?' she came back.

'Some say the devil!'

Smiling like that he was an extremely handsome man, the sombreness gone from his brilliant black eyes and mouth. Jaime sighed a little, then started to laugh, a soft little laugh gurgled in her throat. He looked down at her blue-sheened head and his arm tightened, gathering her in closer to his lean frame. 'Isn't it obvious?' he asked abruptly, catching her eyes. She continued to look up at him but remained silent, her body drawn and curving towards him. Some invisible current was linking them whether they wanted it or not. Her breath almost caught at the way his eyes were travelling over her face.

'Keep talking,' she said in an agitated little voice.

'Perhaps you're right. Where was I?'

'The cousins.'

'Ah well, your cousins Sue-Ellen and Leigh are both very fetching, smart as paint, and they'd both do anything for the family's sake, even marry me. Neither of them work at anything but that.'

'How boring!'

'You might think so, Jaime, they don't. In any case, they fill up their time pretty completely. Simon and Brett are with the firm—company law. They have a lot of assets, so I'm told. Good looks, a big name, no known enemies beyond this room. They would never think of leading a revolt against your grandfather.'

She trembled a little, hopelessly out of her depth, and he glanced at her half amused, half impatient. 'It's best to know this sort of thing, Jamie. You said so yourself.'

'And I'm grateful. You dance beautifully, Quinn. No doubt it's the practice with Sue-Ellen and Leigh.'

'Yes, they'd have me giddy if they could. I thought you were starting to relax. In fact, I thought you were going off to sleep.'

'I'm moving, aren't I?' she protested.

'Not close enough,' he said deliberately, his black eyes gleaming with mockery.

'My aunts?' she prompted.

'Rapacious.'

'Fascinating! It gets worse and worse.'

'I'm only speaking for myself, of course. Many another would tell you they're very stylish ladies, which they are, and they do a lot of good works about which

42

they're fairly voluble. That's how it is, violet eyes. I can feel your heart pounding.'

'I've come to the conclusion I've been living in a little haven of peace,' she remarked.

His jeering taunt touched her cheek. 'Jaime, Jaime, our families have made the economy expand enormously. Think on that and be proud.'

'It's not something to be ashamed of, is it?' she looked up at him directly, her melodious young voice quite crisp with a shadow of his own mockery. He returned her gaze, his own narrowed.

'Not entirely, thank God! You're too bright, Jaime. It might go against you.'

'You don't scorn brightness, do you?'

'Only in females.'

'What man doesn't!' she said sourly.

'Don't be a little shrew!'

'Am I really, how interesting!'

'And a miracle of beauty, femininity, all that sort of thing that bogs a man down.'

'As in quicksand?'

'That's it!' He broke into a laugh that had the true ring of amusement. 'In the entrance hall of Falconer is a pair of seventeenth-century Chinese porcelains, vases about twenty or so inches high. The blue violet of the decoration is the exact colour of your eyes.'

'I simply can't wait to see them!' she said, seeing her reflection in the depths of his eyes.

'Aren't I allowed to express my reverence for beauty?'

'Not at close range!'

'I'm surprised it's affecting you, Jaime.'

'Don't you mean you're delighted? I think you like to make women react.'

'A harmless pursuit, surely?'

43

'Only if one knows the score.'

'Point taken. Naturally I wouldn't think of adding you to my list of—what shall we call them?—victims!'

'It wouldn't work in any case!' she said with great conviction, staring up at him intently.

'Gently, Jaime, gently. There's no need for such a strenuous protest.'

'There's nothing I would dislike more than losing my head,' she whispered with soft violence.

'I'd say you'd better get used to heads toppling all round. A pattern for the future with that face!'

'I'm more than a face, I'm a mind!'

'That's even more dangerous! I can see you're terribly clever,' he teased her.

'And I've noticed you're a hard, mocking devil!'

He nodded his dark head agreeably. 'I'm immune to insults, Jaime. I wasn't the first time, and for years after, but I am now.'

'I don't like it when your eyes flash. I didn't know black eyes could have so much life in them.'

'I could easily reassure you,' he said in his vibrant dark voice.

'That would be equally bad,' she retorted.

'Then you'd better stop flinging down challenges. It's been part of my training to pick them up.'

'But it's all in your mind!' she said sweetly. 'I don't mean anything at all. You're too quick off the mark.'

'I am. It doesn't pay to fumble along.'

The music had stopped and she was standing in the circle of his arms looking up at him. 'Why do you look at me so intently?'

'How do you want me to look?'

'Not so that you make my head swim.'

'That's the wine.'

'I've only had a glass and I'm quite used to it. Derry

and I always have a bottle of wine with dinner.'

'Well then, you're only an infant and infants do have these little problems in adjustment.'

'You mean they've no head for adult games. Shouldn't we be getting back to the table? I'd like some strong black coffee.'

'And you needn't drink alone. As it happens I'm ready for it myself, then I suppose I should be getting you home.'

'Yes, it's dark outside.'

He steered her gently but effectively back to the table, his hands on her shoulders. 'What makes you say the things you do?'

'Cause and effect,' she said lightly. 'Some people make one vivacious.'

'Particularly at nineteen.'

'You obviously didn't take it seriously, what I said about patronising me.'

'I'm sorry, Jaime.' He held the chair for her. 'I just can't help it.'

'You took the words right out of my mouth. Meeting you has been a very *meaningful* experience, as Peter Ustinov would say.'

'There's an hour of the evening left,' he observed.

'No climaxes, please!' she begged him across the table, her eyes just faintly alarmed.

'I can't promise anything, Jaime, particularly when you look at me like that.'

'If that's true, I could take a cab home.'

'Don't think of it! I don't tip little day-old chicks out of the nest.'

'I'm glad. For a moment you filled me with dread.'

'Then don't present two faces—woman and child.'

A curious excitement began to gnaw at her. There was danger in this man: danger in the way he looked, danger in the way he talked, his black eyes highly charged with vivid life. Waiters were gliding around their table and dissolving again into the swirling room with its soft lights and its flowers and women in their prettiest after-dark dresses.

'I have the strangest feeling I've been here before,' she said.

'With me?'

'Yes. Isn't it weird?'

'Do you often feel like that?'

'Don't joke!'

He held up a hand: 'All right then. It's just as unsettling to find I know your face exactly.'

'Ghosts!' she said. 'Only we're here in the present.'

'Little changes, Jaime. I know damned well you could hold a man in thrall just as easily as Rowena did.'

'Ah, you've got your knife out again.'

'I'm not aware of it.'

'Oh yes, you are! You wanted to hurt me. Not a knife, a sword that lies between us.' She could feel the tension in him, his winged black brows coming together.

'For every step forward, we go back two.'

'Actually I think you're trying to push me into my grandfather's arms.'

'Drink your coffee, Jaime. I ordered a liqueur.'

'Did you, what is it?'

'See if you like it,' he told her.

'What I like might be sharply irrelevant with you.' She drank the liqueur quickly.

'That was stupid. Too fast.'

'You'll just have to wait and see whether I pass out or not.'

'You haven't had nearly enough.'

'Exactly. I'm just that little bit afraid of you.'

'You don't look like a coward to me, Jaime. You're positive and aware and I can scarcely take my eyes off you, which won't do at all. Drink the rest of that coffee and we'll go.'

'Aye, aye, sir!'

He paused. 'Is that how you see me?'

'Forget it, I was only being flippant.' She glanced at him briefly and felt a swift onrush of excitement. The thought of her own appalling inexperience suddenly struck her and she bent her small exquisite face over the coffee cup and drank religiously as though it was a potion protecting her against any transgression on his part.

For an instant her expression was transparent and Quinn found himself speaking with a tenderness that was unusual in him except in the presence of his grandmother. 'Jaime, the brave and the beautiful and the anxious little girl darting violet glances at me. You're safe, for God's sake, though I shall probably regret it in the morning.'

'Would you mind explaining what you mean?'

'I'd say you've more than enough imagination. Come along, you've dithered long enough.'

'Anyone would dither with you!' she defended herself.

'You've got that off pat.'

'What is it, your sense of power? Do you like moulding people into shape?'

'I feel you could do with a little control,' he returned.

'Well!' she said, but he didn't answer her, only escorted her very firmly out of the restaurant into the beautiful star-spangled night. 'I want to walk along the beach,' she announced.

'You should be tired.'

'Does that mean the beach is out of limits?'

'Nothing is and never has been. All right, Jaime, you suggested it, the beach.'

'We'll take the car down to the esplanade.'

'Just as you say.'

'You sound as though I'm being unreasonable.'

'No, you're getting better by the minute!'

'That's cheering! You try to like me, I know, but forgetfulness is impossible.'

Quinn unlocked the car door and Jaime slid into the seat and waited for him to come round to the other side. It wasn't pleasant what she was feeling, it was almost painful, and she didn't know whether she would be able to carry it off. No easy friendship was possible between them. Neither of them could be cut off from the past. In the car beside her she recognised it in the set of his head, the little air of relentlessness about him. His profile was as good as perfect, but once again it was darkly remote. He turned to her, his eyes gleaming in the light from the dashboard.

'And what momentous thoughts are occupying you now?'

'Just old pictures flitting through my mind. You have an excellent profile, Quinn. Ascetic, until you turn your head full on.'

'And then?'

'It's a very contradictory face.'

'Yours isn't!' he said a little tersely.

'Try to remember I'm not up to your weight.'

'I've been remembering it all evening.'

'Well then, take the first on your right,' she said helpfully.

'Bossy little thing!'

'This mightn't work out as well as I thought.'

'I feel somewhat like that myself, Jaime,' he confessed.

'All right, take me home. We can go this way just as easily.'

His glance pierced the gloom, raying over her face. 'If you're going to force a beach walk on me, the least you can do is go along with it.'

'Yes, Quinn.'

'It seems to me that was *too* meek!' Suddenly he smiled at her, his maddening first hostility gone. For how long Jaime didn't know, being on a see-saw herself.

Out in the night the stars were blazing, thickly clustered over the ocean, a steady stream of fresh air like balm falling all over them and lingering on their skin and their clothes. Pools of light from the street lights spilled on to the white sand, making little radiant oases at the base of the promenade. Jaime slipped out of her sandals and carried them, feeling the cool firm sand underfoot, dry and crunchy. At this hour of the night the beach was deserted, but it was just as beautiful as under the sun. Maybe more beautiful, more mysterious and elusive.

'I've been happier here than any place else!' she said almost to herself.

Quinn picked up a shell, gave it all his attention, then slipped it in his pocket. 'Yes, it's beautiful any hour of the day, perhaps more urgent at night. I'm glad to escape the deadly rat race if only for a while.'

'Is it so bad?' she asked, stopping to look at him.

'Murderous! Harassing, frenetic, the build-up in tension sometimes is enormous. I wouldn't invite you to join my world, only the toughest survive.'

'Yet you're an ambitious man,' she said.

'Yes, but I can't say it hasn't been a fight to the top. A dirty fight a lot of the time.'

'Does that give you that cold-blooded look?'

'You'll pay for that, Jaime,' he said softly, but she somehow knew he meant it exactly.

'I didn't mean cold-blooded,' she said truthfully, 'more a terrible aloofness.'

'And that's better? If I were you I'd leave it alone.'

She stretched out her arms without looking at him, embracing the night. 'Take a deep breath. Isn't that heavenly?'

The clean beauty of the ocean was rushing for them, the waves breaking and tumbling on to the sand but never quite making Jaime's bare feet. She felt exalted and indescribably sad, with the soft pounding of the sea filling her ears with its own kind of music. Her eyes had become accustomed to the night and she could see the sandcastles the children had made that afternoon. They wouldn't be there in the morning, like dreams, for the tide would come right up to the rock wall.

'Isn't that better,' she cried rapturously, 'the world of surf and stars and salt on the wind?'

'It's real *now*,' he said with a mixture of worldliness and amusement. 'Tomorrow it will be insubstantial. I have too much work to do.'

'You're a madman in a madman's world!' The sea breeze was catching at her hair and she swept it out of its heavy coil.

'There's truth in that!' he said, tempted to catch her up and make love to her but keeping a brake on the sensations her vibrant young beauty was arousing. Her dress in the starlight was a silver blur, her face as pale as a flower, fringed by the inky blackness of her hair. An improbably beautiful girl-into-witch and vaguely exasperating with her young taunts. She was still speaking, fighting a losing but enjoyable battle with the wind in her hair.

'What you're telling me hasn't made things any easier. I've been living all these years in a separate world from yours.'

'In a lost world, you mean,' he said very deliberately.

Jaime glanced over her shoulder and back at him. 'Are you trying to tell me only a man who makes money is important?'

'I assure you a lot of people think it's important.'

'Then they should get out into the fresh air. Recover a sense of proportion.'

'That's what's wrong with them, Jaime, they can't!'

'You talk the same language, don't you?'

'Definitely, but only up to a point. Remember that carefully.'

He sounded a little formidable, but there was a cool sensuality in his voice she couldn't fail to notice. 'When would you expect me to leave?' she asked quietly.

'I'm due back in Sydney in three days.'

'Do you think I could handle them?' She appeared to be addressing the timeless ocean.

'You don't *belong* with them, Jaime,' he responded.

'Yet you expect me to go and live with them for old times' sake—Rowena's daughter come home.'

'That's not overstating it. Only you're not Rowena. There are small differences.'

'There are *big* differences,' she said emphatically, 'and one day you'll all see them.'

'I think we can expect that,' he said, his eyes never leaving her.

'So you see you weren't sent to recover a lost child at all.'

'What, then?'

She had been speaking with soft animation, not looking at him but out towards the first foaming line of the breakers, so that his presence right behind her came as a shock. She wanted to turn and say something, *anything*, but simultaneously his arm closed about her, her head brought back against his shoulder. Pure instinct precipitated a bid for freedom. She brought up her two hands, pushing down on his arm in a vain attempt to break his hold, her self-possession shattered like a falling star.

'You're twenty in three months, Jaime,' he said with smooth mockery. 'A grown woman.'

'Don't tell that to me now!'

'Turn round,' he ordered.

'No, I won't! What you're after is some sort of symbolic act, a surrender.'

'What I'm after, Jaime, is the touch of your mouth. It talks a lot of sense—sometimes.'

'Well, when you put it like that ...'

'Don't misunderstand me. I'm through talking!' He spun her with just a little force right into his arms, cupping her face and turning it up to him with all the skill of a sorcerer.

'If you're going to kiss me, *kiss* me!' she said in defiance, staring up at him with wide, shining eyes.

'You don't want it?'

'I don't want it ... yes, I want it!'

'That's what I thought you said.'

She heard his soft laugh and was glad of it, thinking in her inexperience that a kiss would be only a gesture from this strange, complex man, but the first touch of his mouth started an intolerable showering of sparks,

52

an actual physical ache. There was a droning sound in her ears, a muffled droning, like a frail swimmer predictably and about to be doomed. She no longer cared a hoot what he thought of her, her slender body blazing like bushfire under his hands. It couldn't be that she was out of control. It couldn't be that she was ingenuous or precariously stupid. She was vulnerable to this man and she had recklessly shown it from the very first minute. If she couldn't understand her reaction either, he was proving very conclusively that the mind and the body led different lives.

'Stop kissing me,' she whispered. 'Just *stop*.'

His hands shifted to her shoulders, just barely hurting her. 'The hell with that!'

'This isn't part of the plan, Quinn, is it?'

'What you're asking is, did I set out to kiss you. No, I didn't, but I do get my flesh and blood moments.'

'Then it's for the *cold-blooded*?'

'Do you still think I am?' he asked laconically.

'No.'

'Neither are you. I could make love to you until I'm too old to succumb to temptation, but all it would do is hurt both of us.'

'How?' she asked, throwing discretion to the winds.

'I deal in hard facts.'

'You're stunning!' she said in a near whisper. Her skin was so sensitised that she could still feel his touch when he had half turned away from her. She might still have been clinging to him, her heart striking into his as if it were her preordained destiny. A little frantically now she shook back her hair so that it flowed about her face in silky turbulence. 'It's been a very nice evening, Mr Sterling, but do you mind if we go home now?'

'It's where you belong for tonight!'

Her words seemed to have brought him back from an immense distance. She looked around for her sandals, that one of them or both had thrown down on the sand. She couldn't for the life of her remember which one. 'Don't even think of my coming to Falconer!' she said with pleasurable, renewed hostility, on course again.

'You will!' he said briefly, leaning down and retrieving the small, strappy sandals.

'You're a very strange man. You alarm me,' she said, not even thanking him. She almost ran across the sand, her dress fluttering, and hesitated at the foot of the stairs to slip on her shoes. In another minute she had almost reached the car.

'Stop it, Jaime,' he caught up with her and locked her wrist, flaring excitement at will. 'Come with me and you'll learn a lot in the process.'

'I've learned a lot already!'

'You don't know a damn thing!'

'I know what you've taught me.'

'We won't mention it,' he smiled at her, 'until I kiss you again.'

'Now that's something that won't happen!' she said with almost comical panic.

'How would you set about stopping me?' He sounded as if he was genuinely interested.

'I've a few tricks of my own,' she assured him.

'You don't need any tricks at all. All *you* have to be is exactly you!'

'Thank you,' she murmured with a kind of impotent rage beating at her temples.

'Don't be silly, Jaime, you've no reason to be annoyed with me. I'm not your enemy.'

'You could seriously reverse my fortunes!'

He looked down at her passionate young face, an

odd smile in his eyes. 'You're fascinating, Jaime, do you know that? I wouldn't have missed out on this trip for the world. In a lot of ways it's been a fantastic surprise.'

'Don't congratulate yourself yet!' she said to him with a certain imperiousness.

Quinn smiled and smoothed back the black silky sweep of her hair. 'Don't ever lose that fighting spirit. It's a precious commodity.'

'I'm glad I have it, if there are men like you around.'

'There you go again, and it's fatal!'

'I'll tell you what,' she said purposefully, 'we could strike a bargain. Get in the car and I'll tell you about it.'

'Splendid!' he said, staring into her face. 'You're rather a breathless character, Jaime. A man would have to look high and low for your like!'

He unlocked the car with barely concealed impatience for her to continue, even going so far as to turn on the interior light, his arm sliding along the back of the seat as he trained on her a brilliant black scrutiny. 'Please go on. I keep feeling a shift in our positions. You're a born boss.'

'If I come to Falconer, Quinn,' she said earnestly, 'could you back me in a business venture?'

'Great God, what is this, blackmail?'

'Don't mention that word, it isn't in my vocabulary. I'm not shy and retiring, you can see that; I don't have to be stupidly modest like a Victorian relic, I have real ability. I just know I could be a good designer. You told me yourself you liked this dress.'

'I love it!' he said with black, amused malice. 'But not one half as much as the girl in it.'

'Men are unduly preoccupied with that sort of thing. Please be serious, Quinn.'

'Do you mean to tell me we're going to sit here and discuss *business*?'

'Why not?'

'Why not, indeed! All right, Jaime, fire away. You've got exactly five minutes. But first tell me, why me?'

Jaime's blue eyes were startlingly beautiful, ablaze with enthusiasm. 'It could never be my grandfather, for obvious reasons. That megalomaniac bit has always stuck in my head and I never even knew who he was. I know perfectly well you're too hard-headed to come into anything foolish, but with a little help I could build up a successful business in time. I have a natural flair and I can do everything. The lot! Others have done it, Pru Acton and Jane Cattlin, why not Jaime Gilmore? The ideas just flow out, but precisely nowhere. I have to have help, then I'll work my fingers to the bone to prove myself.'

'I'm indeed glad you mentioned that,' he said dryly. 'One thing you might have overlooked, your grandfather won't allow a moment of your time to be diverted from him.'

'Don't you think I can guess that?' She leaned forward and grasped his sleeve, staring up into his dominant dark face. 'Does my idea make sense to you?'

'Go easy, Jaime! My head's spinning, and not only with your proposal. I mean, I have to mix business with pleasure, but you?' He imprisoned the golden-skinned hand on his sleeve, turning it this way and that as though he could read her future in her palm. 'Beautiful hands, Jaime, neat and elegant like the rest of you. I hate to think of them emaciated through overwork.'

'I've got sketchbooks galore to show you,' she hurried on, 'I make all my own clothes, I've done so for years. I've made clothes for my friends, for nothing of course, they bought the material and I just liked doing it. I've even made a wedding dress and it was absolutely super, everybody said so.'

'My God, and to think I wasn't warned!'

'Take me seriously, Quinn. Please. This really matters to me.'

'A leaf out of the Old Man's book?' he enquired.

'What did you expect, another Sue-Ellen or Leigh?'

'No, I get very tired of them.'

'This is business we're discussing,' she said urgently as the palm of her hand began to tingle.

'Of course, Miss Gilmore. Does your father know of this burning ambition?'

'I've tried discussing it with him many times, but . . .'

'All right, I know the score. Ideas are all very well, Jaime, so is creative ability, but there's so much more to it, and I'd have to see a lot more of your work.'

'You will, I promise you, and once you do I'm sure you'll decide in my favour.'

'Jaime, you're irresistible!' he said, carrying her hand to his mouth. 'The soft sell!'

She frowned. 'Don't spell it out like that! I want nothing but a little strictly legitimate help and encouragement. Everyone needs a patron. Look at Michelangelo and the Pope!'

'Please don't bring them into it, Jaime. I tell you, it's unnecessary.'

'I'm not asking you to back a failure, Quinn. I know I can make it. I just *know*!'

Quinn looked thoughtful. 'It's given to some of us to *know*, Jaime, I can't deny that. That's how we find the strength to get to the top. Let's say for the time being you have me interested, but I promise nothing. You're on trial about a lot of things.'

'So are *you*!' she said, feeling closer to him than

any other human being on earth, which was extremely odd. 'I didn't say I approve of you entirely.'

'Well, you'd better keep quiet about it, or you won't get a penny. Perhaps you could talk it over with my grandmother. She's an extremely clever woman and her taste in all things is superb.'

'She might hate me.'

'She'd never hate you, Jaime, she's above that sort of thing. *Quite uncivilised*, I can hear her saying it. She might, however, stop short at the sight of your face, but I suppose she'll have to get used to it.'

'But for heaven's sake, why shouldn't she bury the hatchet?' she demanded.

'Now you sound nineteen! An ignorant little girl who hasn't seen life.'

'I *am* nineteen, Quinn,' she said in a quick flood of words, her blue-violet eyes shimmering. 'I can't be an all-suffering, sophisticated woman of the world yet.'

'I don't want you to ever be,' he rejoined.

'I expect it will have to happen!'

'Particularly if you're going to set the fashion world on fire,' he grinned.

'Sister Monica always used to say she could teach me anything and I let her, but actually I knew far more about sewing and handling material *then,* than she'll ever know!'

'Poor dear Sister Monica, God help her! Perhaps she should have had a patron.'

'I knew you'd be extremely interested in my proposition,' she said, scarcely hearing him.

'You're convincing, that's for sure! Now, not another word if you don't mind. I'm not all that keen on career women.'

'Let's shake hands on it,' she said, almost feeling the wine of success in her veins.

'I've a better idea.' His hand wound her black hair like a silk rope, drawing her to him. 'I'm not sure you're not unique. You even manage to delight my mind!' Relentlessly he lowered his head with no ordinary gift for making love to a woman, ousting every other thought from Jaime's mind. It was a brief caress, controlled, but it impressed itself deeply on Jaime's consciousness. She didn't attempt to evade him, just turned up her mouth, her lids falling. She was trembling when he released her, staring at him with an almost childlike wonder.

He spoke casually, as though she were a secretary across a desk. 'I'll ring you the day after tomorrow.'

'I never discuss business on the phone. Besides, this is between the two of us.'

'What a good idea, and I'm not even excessively surprised. Now let me get you back to your father.'

CHAPTER THREE

FALCONER was a piece of old England, a beautiful manor house built on the foreshores of Sydney Harbour. Turreted, towered with romantic Gothic windows in jewel colours, its rosy sandstone walls were almost covered with ivy and scented creepers, its terraced gardens sweeping down to the blue harbour, sheltered and enclosed on all sides by magnificent native and exotic trees that soared to such a height that the house was guaranteed a splendid isolation. Built in the 1840s by an important Colonial official, Sir Edward Wyndham, the original brilliant estate had been drastically reduced in size to the present extremely valuable but relatively small block of land, and had passed out of the hands of Sir Edward's descendants and into the vastly enriched hands of Sir Rolf Hunter some thirty years before.

It was without question the most beautiful and romantic house Jaime had ever seen or even dreamed of entering, set like some architectural jewel looking out on to the blue sparkling harbour. Only Quinn's hand beneath her elbow kept Jaime steadily walking towards it. When she had first glanced up after getting out of the car, she had glimpsed a figure at one of the upstairs windows. She was certain it had been a woman, perhaps her Aunt Georgia. Quinn, in turn, glancing down at Jaime, noted the fact that she was extremely nervous and had lost colour; apart from that she couldn't have looked better, polished but casual in one of the incredibly chic and inventive three-piece outfits she had made herself. This one was the colour of young claret, with a beautiful contrasting blouse in a patterned silk which accented the golden tan of her skin and intensified the blue-violet of her eyes until they blazed in her small face. She had an intuitive, highly artistic sense of style, very likely inherited from her father, and she'd be too much for Georgia and Sue-Ellen who loathed competition above all things.

'Steady,' he said, bending his dark head nearer her. 'You look super, to use one of your own words.'

'I feel a complete stranger to myself,' she confessed. 'What am I doing here?'

'Sticking to our bargain, I hope. By the way, don't breathe a word of it, including the fact you're a knockout with the scissors and the sewing machine.'

'I think I'll have my hair cut now I'm in Sydney. They have superb stylists here.'

He smiled and looked down at her. 'Can't you hold on to that black mane? It's very sensuous, to say the least.'

'You'll like what I have in mind,' she assured him.

'I'm sure I will. You're destined to go a long way, Jaime.'

'It's not going to be easy,' she said, with a sudden premonition that touched him as well, for he briefly agreed:

'No.' He looked up towards the house again and his face changed, becoming guarded and faintly saturnine. A woman in a deep sea green caftan was gliding towards them, the sunlight streaming over her beautifully blonded hair.

It was easy to classify her—the wife of a very rich man, all subtle arrogance, her narrow green eyes smiling as they moved swifter than light over Jaime. In a few seconds she was upon them, giving Quinn an intimate smile, pressing a white jewelled hand to his

61

cheek, and greeted Jaime with a high concentrate of attention, then took the girl's hands and kissed her cheek.

'My dear child, you're the image of your mother!' she said as though that covered everything.

'Aunt Georgia!' Jaime responded, trying to fight out of the persuasive fumes of a very expensive and adventurous perfume.

'Welcome to Falconer, my dear,' Georgia offered belatedly, a constriction somewhere under her breastbone. She turned to Quinn almost with relief and linked her hands around his jacketed arm. 'How lovely to have you back again. We've *missed* you,' she said as though he had been to the moon and was back again to a terrestrial paradise. Her green eyes found Jaime's. 'You've no idea how fortunate you were to have Quinn. He's nobody's guide as a rule.'

'He was a lot of fun, actually,' Jaime said in a fit of devilment, which made Georgia's smile chip at the corners.

'Don't let my Sue hear you say that!' Georgia warned playfully. 'She would throw her life away for this man.'

'How wasteful! May I see my grandfather, Aunt Georgia? I'm looking forward to meeting Sue and the rest of the family.'

'As they're anxious to meet you, dear,' Georgia maintained, substituting *avid* for *anxious* in her own mind.

The girl was a shock; Rowena all over again, more poised and well turned out than Georgia could credit with the insignificant background her appalling father had provided for her. Her outfit had everything; cut, line, a wonderful colour with that enviable Queensland tan, and she wore it like a professional model with considerable élan. Rowena's exotic hyacinth gaze mocked her, dominating the young face with its Indian black hair. Georgia was horrified and alarmed. In fact she earnestly wished the child had died with the mother. Rowena had always caused trouble, and her daughter struck the same chord. Georgia turned and led the way with Quinn and Jaime a few measured steps away from her.

Immediately Jaime entered the large entrance hall, her eyes fell on the tall Oriental vases that stood on either side of an eighteenth-century lacquered chest exquisitely decorated in gold and turquoise on a black ground. Long blossoming branches grew out of them, reflected in the Chinese Chippendale mirror that hung above the cabinet. Against the opposite wall were a pair of Chinese armchairs inlaid with mother-of-pearl. They were clearly not intended for comfort, but they were wondrously beautiful. A great bronze doré chandelier hung directly above Jaime's head, the floor was parqueted and covered with a fine Imperial Chinese rug and the magnificent cantilevered stairway, with its elaborate carving and Gothic balusters, marked the beginning of a remarkable art collection that Jaime was to find covered every available wall in the house, and even the specially-lit corners. Reception rooms opened off either side of the hall, but Jaime was not to see them then, for a young woman suddenly winged down the stairway crying a name:

'Quinn, *darling*!'

Jaime stood resolutely, feeling extremely unwanted. With the gift of all females she had defined Georgia's true feelings instantly. Georgia's daughter Sue-Ellen was a sleek and cosmeticised twenty-four-year-old version of her mother. They had similar coloured hair and eyes and similar expressions, though Sue-Ellen's youth saved her. She was flinging herself headlong at Quinn, who took hold of her arms before she latched them round his neck, her fair-skinned face full of a delicious excitement. 'Darling, darling!' she continued breathlessly, not in the least put out by a certain resistance in him.

'Sue, where are your manners?' Georgia chided her fondly. 'Turn around this minute and say hello to your cousin Jaime.'

'Hello, Cousin Jaime!' Sue said without turning her head.

'A welcome, I'm sure, that makes Jaime's heart glad,' Quinn said smoothly.

'Dear me, dear me!' Sue-Ellen gathered herself and spun round and advanced on Jaime with her hand out. 'Welcome to the bosom of the family. You've been an outsider for so long.'

'And looking forward to returning,' Jaime said pleasantly. 'How are you, Sue?'

'Oh, terrific! Maybe the reverse. You're the living image of your mother.'

'So I've been told.'

'Grandfather is going to be very taken with you,' Sue-Ellen said.

'Not odd in a grandparent,' Quinn observed dryly, then shot back the cuff of his shirt and glanced down at his wrist watch. 'I'll take Jaime up to him if I may, Georgia. There are a few things he'll want to know, then I'll be on my way.'

'Surely you're staying for a while. What about dinner?' Sue-Ellen wailed.

'Not this evening.' Quinn expressed his regret with his rare charming smile that hovered for a second only. 'My grandmother is expecting me to dine with her.'

'What happens if you rang up and said you were

dining here?' Georgia suggested, a little in awe of Margo Sterling.

'I wouldn't think of disappointing her, Georgia. If you're ready to meet your grandfather, Jaime, it's this way.'

'I am,' Jaime said quietly, pulsating with nerves and acutely aware of the cynical thoughts that nourished mother and daughter.

'Hurry back, will you, Quinn?' Sue-Ellen begged, 'I'll wait for you here. You're the last man in the world to act nursemaid—surely Jaime can go up by herself. It's the fourth door on the right as you go along the gallery.'

'I think Jaime can have her hand held this once,' Quinn said, his black eyes brilliant and sharp as needles.

'Just charming! How do you do it, Jaime, those big blue eyes?'

'I thought Quinn was just being considerate.'

'Why, Sue, how you talk!' Georgia remonstrated with her daughter. 'I don't know what Jaime will think of you.'

'She'll know soon enough,' Sue said a little viciously, her green eyes narrowed to slits. 'By the way, Uncle Viv and the family have been invited for dinner. A little get-together in Jaime's honour. Sure you won't change your mind, Quinn? Leigh will be *so* disappointed. It's a sort of contest between us.' Her green gaze, transferred to Jaime, was as instructive as a stop light.

'Shall we go up now, Jaime?' Quinn grasped Jaime's arm, quite unconcerned by all the female interest so fervently avowed.

'Yes, *please*,' she said in a soft undertone, honestly considering leaving within the hour.

The gallery was long and beautifully proportioned, hung with paintings and chairs set at intervals, a lovely stained-glass window set at one end through which the sun poured on to the polished floor and the Persian runner. Jaime was beset with a strange nostalgia, a wave of emotion that was making her eyes shimmer. There was nothing for her here in this beautiful house. It would have been better for her never to have come. She tugged on Quinn's arm and he looked down at her, an unaccustomed compassion on his dark, handsome face.

'Where's that refreshing fighting spirit?' he demanded.

'Can't you tell they don't like me? They don't want me here.'

'Did you expect anything else?'

He scrutinised her for a long minute and something in his expression made her put her shoulders back. 'All right, we've come this far!'

'And we'll go all the rest.' His strong arm descended and tightened around her delicate shoulders. 'This is going to be a new kind of life, Jaime, one unknown to you, so that sometimes you'll feel like a different person, but I'm convinced you'd survive any upheaval.'

'Can you tell me why?' she demanded.

'Because basically you're a very strong person.'

'You don't know me.'

'Because it's been only a few days?'

'Quinn?' She looked up at him, for that moment entirely at his mercy, a young girl still, blue glints in her hair, her young face intent, absorbed by the tragic past.

'It's all right, Jaime.'

'Have you been hearing a word I've been saying?'

'God help me, I remember every one of them. Your

grandfather is waiting for you with a full heart and that's the truth. Compassion has been nearly driven out of this family, but you have it. Keep it undimmed until you're an old, old lady with children and grand-children and great-grandchildren who adore you.'

'I don't think I'm ever going to be able to thank you for this,' she said. 'Probably I'll forget it sometimes.'

'You will, with your volatile temper. Turn your face up, beauty like yours is hard to come by and your grandfather will want to see it the very first minute.'

Jaime drew a deep breath, since that was all she could do, and saw Quinn pause outside a solid cedar door that gave on to her grandfather's suite of rooms. He paused for a moment, looking back at her, then he tapped on the lustrous panelling. A woman's voice answered, calling a: 'Come in,' and after a few seconds a pleasant-faced, competent-looking woman in an impeccable white nurse's uniform came to the open doorway.

'How are you, Mr Sterling? Miss Gilmore!' She smiled at Jaime, her brown eyes searching. 'Sir Rolf is expecting you.' She didn't wait for an introduction but went swiftly out of the door and shut it softly behind her.

Jaime could see her grandfather quite clearly, stand-ing against the windows staring at her as though he found her face a thing of more profound beauty than any in history.

'Jaime!'

'Grandfather!'

He shook his silver head, and a terrible sadness covered his face.

It was too much for the tender-hearted Jaime. She covered the space that divided them like a gazelle, flinging out her arms for all her preconceived notions,

67

driven by some force quite outside her, to comfort this old man who was her grandfather. Somehow her own face was pressed to his heart, his hand shaking but inexpressibly tender, shaping the back of her head. 'Little Jaime, and to think I've never known you.'

'Hush, Grandfather!'

'I'll die easily now.'

'You won't die at all. I've only just arrived.'

'So precious, so precious, my granddaughter I've never known. Can you ever forgive me for failing you?'

'I've been happy,' she told him, 'I love my father.'

'Yes, some women are made for devotion. Look up at me, Jaime! Quinn, my dear boy, how can I ever thank you? Mission accomplished as usual.'

'You could let me go ahead with Dinsmore & Donovan. How are you, Sir Rolf, you look a new man!'

'I feel it. You can talk to me later about D&D. Believe it or not, I agree with you. Can't you come to dinner, my dear boy? Bring Margo, of course, though she's never approved of me. We must welcome our youngest member of the family. Isn't she beautiful, the image of Rowena!'

'There are differences if you look for them.'

'Over Nigel, isn't she—Margo?'

'As you're over your daughter. Thank you for the invitation, Sir Rolf. Naturally I'll allow my grandmother to decide. She was expecting me to dine with her.'

'You'd like him to come, wouldn't you, Jaime? After all, he brought you back to me. Great powers of persuasion has Quinn!'

'He must please himself, Grandfather, and consult his grandmother. But yes, I'd like them both to come.'

'Thank you, Jaime.' There was no edge of mockery in that dark, sardonic voice. 'I have a report here I'd like you to look at, sir. No filling in, just the facts.'

Sir Rolf nodded. 'Let's hope you're right.'

'I am right.'

'You're a ruthless young devil, Quinn. All the Sterlings rolled into one.'

There was a hard flicker of anger in Quinn's dark eyes. 'You could never have applied that word to any one of them. I'm the man I am because that's the way I have to be!'

Sir Rolf looked away from him, frowning. 'I'd rather one of my own was that! Don't imagine I don't know what I've got in you, Quinn, a trouble shooter.'

'There's no question of owning me, Sir Rolf.'

'I guess I like to own everybody. You're as arrogant as that fallen angel, you know that? You're the man I pick for all the difficult assignments, but I don't know you, do I?'

Across Jaime's head Rolf Hunter studied his most brilliant executive. No one could touch him in the technical department either. He knew the business from top to bottom; plant, productivity, the latest technology. He was an expert in management. The men all chatted away to him cheerfully when they had never been known to approach his own sons. He could handle the unions as well as government officials and he was liked and respected by every member of the Board outside his own family. The boys—well, it was reasonable for them to hate him. Quinn was clever and strong and so positive when they only knew the language and went through the motions efficiently. It wasn't enough. He should be worried himself by young Quinn Sterling and he would have been even a few years back; now nothing seemed to matter. Making money was no longer important. He had more than enough of it and he would have let it all go to have

Rowena's daughter come home again. Only one mistake he had ever made in his life and it had been colossal. Now he had been given the chance to make reparation.

He smiled at Quinn with ironic appreciation, proud of him in spite of the fact that Quinn was almost as big a fox as he was himself. What happened from now on he couldn't prevent. After his death, somehow Quinn Sterling would gain control, despite all the weapons his sons would bring in and use against him. Besides, there was too much he liked about Quinn himself, though occasionally he caught glimpses of Philip Sterling, his first partner, and was startled by the resemblance.

Philip with his impeccable ideals, Philip the intellectual, the brilliant engineer, with a family who found the young Rolf Hunter just that bit their social inferior though he had been a go-getter then. It had been he who put Hunter Sterling on the map, not Philip with his masterly conceptions. In a lot of ways Quinn was a radical departure from his father and grandfather, but now and again Rolf caught the same aristocratic aloofness in those brilliant black eyes. These days it amused him, though it frightened the boys, Gerard and Viv, out of their wits. His grandsons, so far, were non-events. Magnates were born, one couldn't cultivate them. Quinn Sterling would bring the wheel of fortune full circle.

What Rolf had done to Quinn's father, though provoked, had been damnable. Nothing daunted him in those days. Margo Sterling, a charming and very cultivated woman to this day, stared right at and through him, yet she had loved Rowena. Well, Rowena on whom she had lavished such affection repaid her cruelly. Margo had a son, Nigel. Life was hard. Families made one suffer. Was it any wonder he turned to business? He had made it everything up to now.

Jaime, the silent observer, looked from her grandfather to Quinn. Both of them were very striking men, much of a height, which meant over six feet, her grandfather with a full, pure silver head of hair and flaming black eyebrows, dark grey eyes like a piece of steel; Quinn with the sparkling arrogance of achievement and a look of breeding, contemptuous of hypocrisy, his black eyes flashing with complete directness, as relentless in his fashion as Rolf Hunter was in his. Both of them had tremendous charisma, and a genius for seeing right through to essentials, shutting out everything else. Both of them with an air of power, stronger now in the younger man and for a number of reasons. Rolf Hunter was coming quickly to the end of his life and he had almost forsaken the business empire he had built up.

'Grandfather?' Jaime, feeling suddenly protective of him, put out her hand to this lion of an old man and he took it and held it tightly, his wonder and peace increasing every minute he gazed at her face. 'We've so much to talk about. When I get changed, can we walk in the garden? It looks incredibly beautiful, and the harbour!'

'It's nothing ... *nothing*, compared to your face!' For an instant Sir Rolf looked transfixed, his mind in the past. 'I always knew you'd come back, Rowena.'

Jaime couldn't move or speak, taken utterly by surprise. Quinn moved suddenly, taking a manilla folder crammed with typed pages out of his briefcase and slapping it down on the writing desk near the window. 'I'd like you to read this, Sir Rolf. We'll lose money if you don't!'

'Money, money!' Sir Rolf cried affably. 'All right,

71

my boy. I'll do just as you say and thank you once again.'

'No thanks needed at all,' Quinn said briefly. 'It was a pleasure. Now if I have to get to the city and then back to Rosemount I'd better hurry. I'll see you again, Jaime.'

Jaime lifted her small head high, bewildered by some razor-sharp note in his voice. 'Tonight, I hope,' she looked up at him gravely, her blue eyes magnetic in her golden face, but she didn't move away from her grandfather.

'I'll convey your invitation to my grandmother,' he said with exquisite courtesy, studying both their faces with a kind of sombre intensity as though marking them for ever. She had thought he despised all her family, and maybe this would be true of her as well. She was at a loss with him, uncertain, back to square one. If she wanted to go with him, and she did, she gave no sign of it, locked to her grandfather's side, appearing extremely young and graceful beside him.

Quinn moved to the door, turned quickly to salute them, then he was gone. His strength and authority, the mingled protectiveness and antagonism, whatever it was he felt for her, seemed to go with him. She was on her own and she would have to know how to cope.

When Quinn arrived at Rosemount, he found his grandmother waiting for him with singular, distressed curiosity. With his arm around her shoulders, he led her into the drawing room, exclaiming over the beauty of her hair which she had had specially shampooed and set that day to mark his homecoming. She listened to his compliments solemnly but with great pleasure, for she went to a great deal of trouble with her appearance when her arthritis these days often had her in

72

indescribable pain. Enthroned in her favourite wing-backed chair, she waved her grandson into the chair opposite, searching his lean handsome face with pride and an insatiable need to hear about this girl, Jaime. Such an odd name for a girl, but that would have been her father's contribution.

Quinn took her hand, his eyes wandering over Margo's infinitely dear face. A beauty in her youth, the signs were still there in plenty—the indestructible bone structure, the breeding, the spirit and the intelligence. Once her eyes had been an overwhelming blue, not the exquisite lapis lazuli of Jaime's, but the blue of the sea; now they were faded, soft and cool like the sky seen through rain. She had great courage. She had known tragedy, losing her husband and two of her children, but she had survived and her will was like iron.

'Tell me,' Margo said abruptly, in her rather deep voice. 'Is she as lovely, as enchanting as Rowena?'

'I almost yearn to tell you she's as plain as a wall-flower, but she's everything Rowena was and more.'

'I find that highly painful. Do you think I'm awful, darling?'

'No, I don't. They want us to join them for dinner, by the way. A celebration.'

'Oh no!'

'There's no need to go.'

'I'll come right out with it, I can't stand them. Why should that man be rewarded, that wicked old man?'

'I think he's repenting,' Quinn soothed.

'Life is full of surprises. What he did to your father, not Philip so much, but your dear father, I'll never forgive him!'

'I can attend to that little problem,' Quinn said austerely.

'I'm not sure if I approve of that either.'

'Then you'll have to get used to it, darling. I'm the tycoon, not you!'

'Oh, Quinn!' she said, and touched his cheek. 'The old stories, they're tragic, are they not?'

'They've never made me laugh. Jaime, too, has had a struggle. It hasn't been easy for her. Her father is talented, but not serious about anything except maybe revenge. He's never forgiven Rowena, either!'

Margo nodded. 'Poor Rowena, I wonder if she lies easily in her grave. She was still so young when she died. From the minute she married him things went badly.'

'It's impossible to dislike him. He has a lot of charm and I'm quite sure he could have been a much bigger success with just a little drive!'

'Not everyone enjoys success, my darling boy. Success carries difficulties and responsibilities, bigger and bigger worries.'

'Well, I'm not going to stop here,' Quinn said, swiftly and completely.

'That's no news!' Margo Sterling smiled at her grandson, studying him for that instant quite objectively. 'I know your grandfather would think some of the things you've been doing lately were dangerously unsuitable!'

'Grandfather completely lacked my business judgment.'

'I know that! Poor Philip, he found the world of intrigue and counter-intrigue quite impossible.'

'That's why we lost out progressively to Hunter. For years he got away with the lot, but not now. It's all over!' He was staring into the past, his handsome dark face grim, his lean strong hands moving as though he contemplated wringing someone's neck. 'I even have

74

to steel myself to accept the rest of them as vastly over-paid executives.'

'Look here, Quinn,' his grandmother said sternly, 'they're entitled to their share of the multi-million-dollar business their father and grandfather built up.'

'Not the lion's share!' Quinn said pleasantly, his black eyes brilliant. 'They've had that for too long.'

'Don't think they're not aware of their position. They'd hurt you if they could. Everyone knows you're running Hunter Sterling these days. It's extraordinary how that man has lost all interest in what once was his whole life.'

'The change is Jaime,' Quinn said bluntly. 'If you could have seen his face! Fascinating. The first and only time I've seen him reach out towards another human being and mean it.'

'Then you don't really remember Rowena, how could you? He adored her, so much so that her brothers could scarcely endure her. It was no secret that he paid little attention at all to the boys when they were small. They've never forgotten it, or their jealousy of their sister. One can feel some pity for them—in a way it's affected their whole lives. Their mother was so gentle, such a defenceless, beautiful creature, she just gave up and died. She never understood her husband. Never for a moment. I know, because she told me. She asked me also, to look after her daughter!' Margo Sterling sighed deeply and her frail crippled hands moved restlessly in her lap. 'Perhaps I can do her daughter a service. But not now. It's cruel, but I don't think I can lay eyes on the child. I'm too old, you see. I might weep.'

'I've never seen you weep,' Quinn said calmly, an expression on his face few but his grandmother had seen. 'What was it Father used to say? There's no one

75

more capable of meeting any situation than my mother!'

'That was years ago, darling, I could very easily blemish my record these days. I'm an old woman and I mean *old*!'

'And you're terribly tough! Where do you think I got it from? Quick, make the decision and I'll abide by it. I just don't know myself.'

His grandmother stared at him. 'That's a first for you! What is she, this Jaime?'

'A witch with long black hair and unnaturally beautiful eyes.'

'You're talking about Rowena,' his grandmother said strangely.

'No, Jaime. She won't go the same way as her tragic mother. She has enormous reserves and she's only a young girl. She's even made it clear to me that she expects me to back her in a business of her own.'

'Why, how peculiar!' Margo Sterling had some difficulty keeping a slight hostility out of her voice. 'That's the Hunter business instinct. It's skipped a couple of generations to Jaime.'

Quinn looked back at her steadily. 'Why on earth shouldn't it? Jaime has big plans. She wants to be another Pru Acton.'

'That's a tall order.'

'The raw material is there, if you'll forgive the pun. I'd like you to speak to her. She's too high voltage at the moment, but she'll learn. Her sense of style is innate and enviable. She's very chic, very modern but elegant, and she makes all her own clothes. She expects to have to work very hard and she requires listening to. She has the talent, plus the drive.'

'And she wants you to do the rest! What about her grandfather? He has a tremendous amount of money.'

76

'That would be involving herself in a real dilemma, and she's shrewd enough to know it.'

'It doesn't really affect me, Quinn,' Margo Sterling said, almost pathetically desperate.

Quinn smiled. 'Don't opt out, darling. I know what I'm asking of you. Perhaps not tonight, but spare her a little time. She hasn't had a fortunate life up to now, though she's very loyal to her father.'

'You would seem to have become very loyal to her in a very short time,' the old lady observed.

'She's a child!' Quinn said rather wearily. 'I'm not going to fling her headfirst into the maelstrom. Georgia and Sue hated her on sight.'

'Then we'll go,' Margo Sterling said, equally forceful. 'You said the very thing to attract my sympathy. But then you know that, you cunning devil!'

'Anyway, you ought to take that new hairstyle out. I can honestly say that fellow you go to is an artist.'

'And I don't begrudge him a farthing of his turnover, though some people get quite annoyed.'

'Like Aunt Lucille?'

'That's right. Now, my boy, help me up. If we must go out on this errand of mercy I'll need time to prepare. At times you remind me altogether of my own father. He was always getting us to do unimaginable things without putting himself out one bit!'

'I suppose you enjoyed it.' Quinn said, smiling, but his grandmother only rested against him for a moment and patted his cheek. It would take all her calm and indomitable will to meet Rowena's daughter: Rowena, whose actions had robbed her of a son. Of course Nigel had become morbidly sensitive, but he had been young without the balance of maturity, and Rowena had been such an exceptional girl, an exact blend of the witch Nigel had always called her and a woman to set the nerves pulsing. It would be like resurrecting the old tragedy to meet her daughter, yet it had for Margo a compulsive fascination. She went up to her room on Quinn's arm only wishing to get it all over. It was so very tedious to be old.

CHAPTER FOUR

By the time dinner was over, Jaime felt a little better. It had been something of an ordeal, not only for her, but for the suffering, regal old lady who sat opposite her, her beautifully dressed head high, her misty blue eyes full of pain. It was so unfair, in its way, this resemblance she had to Rowena, for the mother Jaime had never known had made many people unhappy. At times, under the clamorous, glittering eyes of her relatives, she had felt herself akin to the fox with the whole frenzied pack after her. Her uncles Gerard and Vivian, sharp-eyed and handsome, their expensive-looking wives, her cousins Sue-Ellen and Leigh, with their vaulting ambitions, could be dangerous to her, deeply involved as they were in holding and maintaining their positions in Sir Rolf's life and when that life flickered out, in his will.

Her male cousins, smooth-faced versions of their fathers, were making it blatantly obvious they were prepared to consider her as a matrimonial prize the winning of which would be an enormous feather in their caps, both socially and financially, for Sir Rolf was making no secret of his tremendous pride and joy in his newly-found granddaughter. No one was left in any doubt that a new heiress had just been created. It was like having a beautiful dream blown up in their faces.

Only Quinn and his grandmother held themselves aloof, making suave and witty conversation, coming to Jaime's assistance whenever she needed it, and she found she did to combat the family's rapacity. For this she silently thanked them in her heart, not knowing that

79

her beautiful eyes were conveying to Margo Sterling, at least, her sensitivity, compassion and deep gratitude.

It was these qualities, so easily recognised in Jaime, that enabled Margo to get through the evening, for Jaime was so like her mother that it had been like a physical blow, knocking her off balance and sweeping her back in time. A sudden impulse had seized Margo at the first moment of meeting and caused her to put her arms around the girl and kiss her cheek tenderly, a gesture Jaime was destined never to forget, for she had been shocked at the concealed misery in those softly blue faded eyes. Quinn had looked at her with mingled mockery and congratulation, for even he had wondered how his grandmother would react. She had been known to freeze people at a glance, but only if she considered they deserved it. Jaime obviously did not deserve to suffer for the havoc her mother had caused, if only in Margo Sterling's eyes. Jaime was too well hemmed in by her relatives and their burning, hidden fears and antagonisms. They who had so much, yet wanted more. Jaime, who had lived precariously for so many years, would be denied even the smallest legacy from her grandfather if the family had anything to do with it.

The assessment, though harsh, was quite accurate. Sir Rolf's heirs were in complete agreement about Jaime. She was enormously unwanted, though they were scrupulously polite to her in clear view and ear-shot of Sir Rolf. Many furious words had been said in the privacy of their own homes. It was considered not inconceivable that the Old Man, in an excess of stupid reparation for old wrongs, could *over*-compensate the girl, and it was their unpleasant duty to see that this didn't happen. Old people nearing the end of their lives invariably became maudlin about such things. The girl was an outsider, for all Rowena had been her mother. Rowena had surrendered her claim and that of her daughter, choosing her own way, and the family were markedly disinclined to accept Jaime much less take her to their hearts. The sight of Sir Rolf making such a fool of himself further repulsed them. One would have thought he didn't have two other beautiful granddaughters to dote on, and he had never been known to do that, not even when they had been the most adorably cute toddlers in their exquisite little hand-made dresses.

It was unthinkable. They hadn't really believed it until they saw it with their own eyes, but Jaime was emerging as a colossal threat to all of them. Perhaps even on a grander scale than Quinn Sterling with his frightening rise to the seat of power. Sabotage on two levels—small wonder they were so upset and worried. The only ray of light, or the only possible way about the whole bad business, was to marry the girl off to one of the boys. Simon or Brett, it didn't really matter which. They were interchangeable and their dedication to family interests was the only remarkable thing about them.

Margo Sterling, watching all of them with her wise, old eyes, was hopelessly disgusted. Only one thing saved her from total despair; there was an added strength and humour to Jaime's features beside the purity of Rowena's. She hadn't noticed it immediately, so overcome had she been, but now, hours later, she began to appreciate the subtle differences between Jaime and her memories of the young Rowena. The very best of Rowena plus something very individual. One could never have seen Rowena, for instance, ever contemplating setting up her own business. Rowena had been reared a princess. Jaime had come up the hard way and it hadn't hurt her. The end product was

81

a very striking young creature indeed, with courage and ambition, and the others were green with jealousy, the women busy deploring her beautiful face and figure, not realising that they had to give Jaime credit for the chaste little evening dress she had on, sheer as blue smoke, totally demure and inexpressibly stylish, sheening as it did her beautiful young body.

Now Margo realised with a flutter of relief that it might be a good thing to back Jaime in a business enterprise, and the pleasure and intensity of her emotion astonished her. She would talk to the girl, but for tonight she was experiencing too much remembered pain. She would have to arrange with Quinn to bring Jaime to Rosemount. Tonight her ghosts were haunting her, practically sitting beside her. Nigel, as beloved and familiar to her as Quinn was now; Rowena, so beautiful and enchanting that she could do no wrong. Then as now Rowena was Rolf Hunter's only blind spot, and Rowena lived on in her daughter. The situation was potentially dangerous, for even a man as brilliant as Rolf Hunter could still be as big a fool as any other man on earth. He had the power to make Jaime one of the richest young women in the country and in so doing throw a giant scare into his family, and he was a man without pity. Jaime would bear the brunt of his measures, a bigger and bigger rival every minute she stayed on at Falconer.

An hour later, Margo signalled to her grandson that she was ready to go. She had never enjoyed the Hunters' bitter world, as luxurious as were their surroundings, the glittering possessions, the literal fortune in paintings that hung on every wall. Very few people would ever bother to remember that Rolf Hunter had once been a struggling young university student with numerous paying sidelines to support himself and his

82

widowed mother. A man could be a mixture of things, good and bad. It was only when he entered the jungle of big business that Rolf Hunter embarked on the course of ruthless slashing and parrying and back-stabbing that took him right to the top. He was clever. He was extraordinary. He was even a very handsome old man, but Margo Sterling had decided as always that she couldn't stand another minute of his company.

She was conscious of Jaime's presence by her side and inexplicably it now gave her a deep sense of ease. The family had all formed into a group to say goodbye, the girls Sue-Ellen and Leigh, enough alike to be sisters, vying as usual for a minute of Quinn's time. He preferred Leigh of the two, a softer, more amiable version of Sue-Ellen and very attractive tonight in a cool, halter-necked dress the same fresh green as her eyes, her hair like her cousin's with a deep fringe and swinging in casual blonde perfection just clear of her shoulders. Margo much preferred Leigh as well. Given a different background Leigh could relax and be herself, not the member of a clan whose purposes and way of life dominated her.

Leigh more and more, was coming under the influence of her younger but more cunning and selfish cousin, Sue-Ellen. Both girls were affronted by Jaime's beauty and obvious self-confidence. It put them in a rage. The family had pointed out that the girl had almost been dragged up by a failure of a father; it was therefore demoralising to be confronted by a poised and elegant young woman who regarded them all gravely and with a faint element of—*pity*? It was easily seen that their grandfather, who had never loved them and rarely smiled at them, had found again the one person in the world he could love. They all found it frightening and disquieting, though they did their best to be agreeable, with a lifetime's practice at playing it smart.

In their hearts they knew there was no question of getting used to the situation but reversing it. They would never surrender their position, Jaime would have to be the one to go. In a family used to high strategy, dominated by a fierce pride to emerge victorious, one young girl on her own should present no real problem. Rowena had run out on her father and all that she had known. Her daughter could be made to do the same.

After a month of her relations, Jaime felt as though she was drowning in poison. It was such a wild idea to have thought they might accept her. They never would—jealousy brought out the worst in people. The women put this across with force and clarity, smiles on their narrow arrogant mouths. Her uncles Gerard and Vivian kept her constantly under surveillance, their eyes loaded with speculation as though beating their combined brains out to devise some way of rendering her permanently harmless. Her cousins, Simon and Brett, figured largely in their plans, for had Jaime accepted all their numerous invitations to go sailing, swimming, partying and what-not, she would have been as dizzy as a child on a merry-go-round. They were all so alike in their objectives that they might have been one.

There seemed no time whatever to think of her own plans, for her grandfather rarely let her out of his sight. Blood, she had cause to know, was thicker than water, because she found herself indulging him, caught into the desire to please him, or more accurately give him peace, for his health after such a serious heart attack had markedly declined. It was always sacrifice, she thought to herself. Men seemed to demand it. First her father, now her grandfather and her woman's compassion kept her enslaved. Nevertheless it would have to stop.

Quinn, whom she saw fairly often, had been almost formidably abrupt at their last meeting, contenting himself with hurling at her one question: 'When do you intend breaking out of your prison?'

She hadn't answered him then, upset by the cold brilliance of his eyes, but she proposed to do so now. Directly after breakfast, she intended to take a taxi into the city and waylay him in his office. It was true Uncle Gerard and Simon would be leaving in the car shortly before then, but she had no wish to ask either of them for a lift even though the chances were she would run into them at the Corporation Building.

Neither Georgia nor Sue-Ellen ever came down for breakfast, her grandfather had a tray in his room, so Jaime usually endured breakfast with her uncle and cousin. It seemed incredible to her that her Uncle Gerard could have no feeling for her. They shared a family resemblance, but that meant nothing. It wasn't as though his behaviour was uncivilised, quite the reverse; he was extremely convivial, especially in front of his father, but the Judas light shone in his eyes.

It was devastating but true, and small wonder her mother had left home. After a month Jaime had come to realise that her relatives expected her to join them or they would destroy her. It was brutal, but apparently it was their way of life. If she consented in time to marry either of her cousins they would consider her in another light. For then her inheritance, and it was now certain she would receive one, could be kept in the family. Not a one of them had a guilty conscience, for family alliances kept empires alive and they were already under attack from the Sterlings.

Jaime was given to understand that she had better

choose her side, and only a fool would run to the Sterlings. She would never be allowed to use any future financial power against her own family. Even now Quinn Sterling was dictating policy and ran Hunter Sterling, when their father had built the firm up into the great business enterprise it was today. Too many had already assigned their holdings to Sterling, and if Jaime inherited a very large block of shares and for whatever reason assigned them to Sterling, then the family would lose out on the majority shareholding. It was not to be borne.

When Jaime came down that morning, she found the breakfast-room occupied, the sun streaming through the great plate glass window; a modern touch, affording the most beautiful views of the garden and the blue harbour beyond. Gerard Hunter looked up with a smile, laying down his paper, and greeted her most genially. Simon jumped to his feet, pulled out a chair, saw Jaime seated, and offered to serve her from any one of the silver chafing dishes that lined the sideboard. Both men, she had discovered, ate a very hearty breakfast—fruit juice, cereal, a hot dish, eggs and bacon, sausages, grilled tomatoes, enormous quantities of toast and marmalade, excellent black coffee reduced by cream. It almost hurt her to watch them, for she found breakfast the least inviting meal of the day.

Jaime returned their greeting, smiling at Simon, who was looking at her with quite unfeigned admiration. She requested black coffee with toast and heard Uncle Gerard launch into the daily and quite serious lecture on the importance of a good breakfast, involving blood levels and sugar, or blood sugar levels; she never did listen, and felt like pointing out kindly that she was in perfect health notwithstanding. Uncle Gerard suffered from severe migraine and an incipient ulcer, but to

86

comment on that would have pleased no one, so she simply tuned out.

'And what's on the agenda today?' Simon was asking, placing her coffee cup near her right hand, having rung for fresh toast.

'I'm going into the city today!' Jaime said, inadvertently disclosing her intentions, rattled as she was by Simon's heavy breathing. Now he would be sure to offer to drive her there, which he did.

'I'll take you,' he said promptly, giving her his usual embarrassing amount of attention. 'Where is it you want to go?'

'I want to see Quinn,' she said, something of a trouble-shooter herself.

'Sterling?'

Both men almost shouted her down. Uncle Gerard glared at her and came right out into the open, so severe was his shock.

'Yes, I want to talk to him!' Jaime explained artlessly.

Simon stared at her for a full ten seconds. 'He'll be busy, dear,' he said spitefully. 'Don't you know he's a very important man? One has to make an appointment weeks in advance to see Quinn. I should know, I spend practically all of my life trying to arrange a meeting.'

His father's anger was real and so obvious. 'What on earth would you want to see Sterling about?'

'Surely that's my affair, Uncle Gerard.'

The remark only served to further enrage him. 'Look here, young lady,' he cried pompously, in an achingly loud voice, 'it's time you and I had a talk! I consider Quinn Sterling our enemy!'

'I thought he was a partner in the firm.'

'You know nothing whatever about the true situation. Nothing whatever about big business.'

'It must be an inherited trait,' Jaime said calmly. 'I want to speak to Quinn about my own business.'

'Then kindly take my word for it,' her uncle shouted, still misunderstanding her, 'and I'm not going to spell it out again, Quinn Sterling is out to do us all harm.'

At that very moment the housekeeper came in with the fresh toast and there was a necessary little pause, simply burning with frustration. Jaime smiled at the woman and thanked her, and they all waited until she could reasonably be expected to be out of earshot. Gerard Hunter started out again, becoming more and more angry, giving his accumulated anxieties of the past month and more, full rein.

'I expect you, Jaime,' he said forcefully, 'to tell me exactly what you intend to discuss with Sterling. We know, of course, of your visits to Rosemount.'

'I've made no secret of them. May I remind you, Uncle Gerard, I'm a free agent, not some unfortunate employee, and I'm a guest in my grandfather's home.'

Gerard Hunter held up his hand and tried belatedly to gain control of himself. Why, the insolent little chit sounded exactly like the old man! 'If you're determined to misunderstand me, Jaime——'

'Oh, really, Dad, give the poor girl a go,' Simon protested, alarmed at the way things were going. 'You see, Jaime, there are aspects of this you couldn't possibly know about. It should suffice for Dad to tell you Quinn Sterling is no good. He intends to take over Hunter Sterling, and that we'll never allow.'

'We're talking at cross purposes,' Jaime said quietly. 'I wish to speak to Quinn about setting up my own business.'

Gerard Hunter's heavy handsome face flushed a dark red. 'Your *own* business?' he asked with ludicrous disbelief.

Simon leaned forward, laughing. 'Tell us?' he begged with mock urgency.

'I intend to become a dress designer.'

'A dressmaker?' her uncle wailed incredulously. 'Why, my dear girl, you'll make a holy show of us!'

'A dressmaker, how freaky!' Simon crowed.

'Yes, a dressmaker, like Pru Acton and Norma Tullo. Mary Quant and Zandra Rhodes, Schiaparelli and Coco Chanel!'

'Don't draw on those names!' Simon said waspishly, looking very much like his sister.

'Why not? I have ability. I'm prepared to work just as hard.'

'No woman of our family need work!' her uncle proclaimed disdainfully. 'If you must do something, your aunt heads a dozen different committees. I'm sure she could find something to keep you out of mischief!'

'Mischief isn't my scene, Uncle Gerard. Work is necessary for me. I could never be content to live out the easy life. I want to have a goal in life.'

'Have you had any training?' he asked coldly.

'I know what I'm about,' she rejoined. 'I've always known, just like some people know they're going to be singers, or concert pianists or doctors.'

'How marvellous!' Simon cooed, staring intently into her blue-violet eyes. 'But pray tell us, how does Sterling fit into all this? He's an unlikely partner for a dressmaker.'

'He's the best brain I know,' Jaime said flatly. 'I can't bother Grandfather with business matters. He's not nearly well enough.'

'Thank you for nothing, dear!' Simon said sweetly. 'How very generous of you.'

'You did ask me,' she pointed out.

'I also think you'll regret it,' her uncle intervened.

89

'*You* may have forgotten it, young woman, but Sterling hasn't. You're a Hunter!'

'Correction. My name is Gilmore,' Jaime said.

'It could so easily have been Sterling!' Simon mocked her. 'You've heard about poor old Nigel, haven't you? That old boring tale?'

'Maybe my idea of boring doesn't match yours. I respect Quinn's judgment. I'm very fond of his grandmother. She's been very kind to me.'

'Don't let the reason for that pass you by!' Gerard Hunter said sneeringly. 'You're pitifully naïve!'

'An ulcer is too high a price to pay for wisdom.'

'How dare you!' her uncle burst out volcanically.

Jamie stared at him. 'Make no mistake, Uncle Gerard, I'm aware of your hostility.'

This, and the reminiscent set of her head, set a warning thrill through him. He fought to resume his mask of spurious affability and discretion, 'How could you, my dear! You're my niece, my own sister's child. It appals me to hear you say such a thing. We've done everything, *everything* we could to make you welcome. The girls have introduced you to their friends. The boys have taken you everywhere. At the end of the month we're throwing a big party to introduce you to the best people!'

'I can meet a lot of nice people on the bus or the ferry. Anyway, that was my grandfather's idea and I'm only going along with it to please him.'

'You're trying very hard to do that, aren't you, pet?'

'I don't have to try at all!' Jaime said bluntly.

A sudden passion of callous jealousy stared out of Gerard Hunter's eyes. 'Don't be too confident, my dear.'

Jaime looked away from him out on to the beautiful garden with its magnificent shade trees and blossoming shrubs. 'The close family relationship seems to have cracked wide open,' she said with sad irony, 'fallen apart. In a way it's a relief!'

Simon reached for her hand and pressed it affectionately. 'Listen, pet, this is so undignified. We simply don't know what you mean. We're only trying to protect you, to warn you about Sterling, and this is the way you thank us! You must apologise to Dad. You've offended him. Don't waste your life on your silly, girlish ambitions. I've no doubt you made nice little dresses for your dolls. In any case, I've already made up my mind about you.'

'Really, in what way?' she enquired.

'Lunch with me today and I'll tell you. I won't listen to any excuses!' Simon turned back to his father, his voice rallying. 'How could you bark at the poor girl, Dad? She's lost all her colour under that gorgeous tan.'

'I say, I *am* sorry,' Gerard Hunter maintained. 'You have gone pale. Forgive me, my dear.' He tried a frank smile. 'It's only that we know what's best for you. I can understand your desire to do a job of work, but there's absolutely no need to embark on a business career. Why, you'll be married in less than a year.'

'Why wait as long as that?' Simon said gaily, his eyes sparkling and hugely intrigued. 'Now I'm going to pour you another cup of coffee, Jaime, that's gone cold. I'll be set to leave in another twenty minutes.'

'I won't be ready then.'

'I'll wait longer if it will make things easier for you.'

'Thank you, Simon, but it's not necessary. Perhaps I'd better ring through and make an appointment to see Quinn. Thank you for the suggestion.'

'You're going to persist with this?' her uncle demanded, glancing bitterly at his son.

'Undoubtedly. I intend to succeed in life, Uncle Gerard.'

'Unlike your mother and father.'

'My father enjoys every day of his life. Do you?'

'Don't speak to Dad like that,' Simon said heatedly. 'He's not used to it.'

'Put it down to my pathetic naïvety,' returned Jaime.

'It would be interesting to see what you make of yourself at that!' Simon said, staring at her in his febrile fashion.

'Come, Simon, we'll be late!' His father rose with dignity, folding his napkin neatly beside his plate. 'Don't imagine, young lady, that you'll be striking out on your own. Quinn Sterling is a highly skilled manipulator of people. He isn't to be trusted, and this time he's gone too far. Do you really think my father would want you to bypass him for Quinn Sterling?'

'I'm sure Grandfather, like you, would prefer me to lead a life of leisure, surrounded by luxury. It sounds great, but in actual fact it doesn't seem to work out. There's beauty in hard work. Salvation. I believe it's necessary if only to keep us on course!'

'How quaint!' Simon said as though he had given a great deal of thought to the matter. 'I find it enormously boring!'

'Your aunt will be horrified,' Gerard Hunter intoned.

'Whatever for?' Jaime looked up at him.

'You know perfectly well what I mean. This idea of yours is extraordinary. I mean, a tatty dressmaker!'

'Would you call the suit I have on tatty? The dress I had on last night? It inspired my cousins to stare at me all evening. Leigh wouldn't rest until I told her where I bought it.'

'You mean you made it yourself?' Simon said incredulously. 'You're not such a fool as I took you for.'

'*I'm* not the fool, Simon!' She looked back at him levelly.

'This is lovely, a dressmaker in the family! Wait until I tell Mother. Tell me, are you going to use Falconer as your premises?'

'I won't tell you anything at all,' Jaime returned crisply. 'I didn't really expect you to be interested, much less wish me luck!'

'Have you spoken to my father?' Gerard Hunter looked down his fine, straight nose at her, bitterly shocked.

'Not as yet, but I will in my own good time.'

'I'll speak to him,' he retaliated with cold ferocity.

'I'm sure you will, Uncle Gerard, but have a care. It will do you no good at all to criticise me.'

'Ah!' he released a long choking breath. 'Could you be threatening me?'

'Not at all! I'm like you, Uncle Gerard, I'm only trying to point out the dangers.'

Resolutely he walked away from the table, a most peculiar expression on his face. 'I'm leaving in exactly ten minutes, Simon. Are you coming with me or are you taking your own car?'

'I'll come with you,' Simon said instantly with considerable sympathy. 'There are things we need to discuss.'

After his father had left the room Simon lingered for a moment longer. 'It's hard to go against the strength, pet. You'd better pick your side.'

'I have already.'

'Then don't say you weren't warned. You know, Jaime, you're an endless temptation until you open your mouth. Women aren't cut out to be tycoons and they never will be.'

Jaime flared up. 'Don't you believe it! It's only now that women have come to take a great pride in their talents or even been allowed to. We've arrived and we're here to stay. Don't worry, it's no big disaster. It's the men who have to answer for the state of the world as it is today—no temptation for a woman to bring children into it.'

'You're irrational, over-emotional!' Simon accused her, sounding quite overwrought.

'Believe that and you'll believe anything! Run along, Simon. Don't keep your father waiting. I notice you're exceptionally dutiful, or is that the impression you want to create?'

He shrugged and a very hard expression came on to his face. 'You're a very clever girl, Jaime. I can almost admire you.'

'I know. I'm hoping my mind will cancel out my other attractions!'

'I doubt it! Lunch?'

'No, thank you.'

'You'd better leave Quinn Sterling well alone. Either Sue or Leigh would scratch your eyes out.'

'A jungle, is it not?' she said.

'And it's you who'll finish up licking your wounds!'

Jaime forced herself to smile at him. 'You've got the slogan the wrong way around; *Right* is might!'

'Boy, are you the new girl!'

She nodded. 'I suppose I am, but that's the way I'm going to do it.'

'Then you won't worry us. Ever hear the sad tale about Honest John Sterling? A very aristocratic and highly ethical man. Given his head Honest John would have ruined us, by cleaning up here and there, instead

Grandfather brought him to his knees.'

'Apparently Quinn's sorting that one out!'

'You're quick to defend him, aren't you? He doesn't need you, little girl. Quinn is unique among the Sterlings. A brilliant, complex man with tremendous energies, infinitely tougher than all his ancestors put together.'

'You sound as if you admire him, in a grudging sort of way,' remarked Jaime.

'He's bringing the Corporation on in leaps and bounds.'

'Then shouldn't you go down on your knees and thank him?'

'That's likely!' Simon jeered. 'Remember the name, dear, *Hunter* Sterling? Quinn might start demanding an entirely different arrangement. Sterling Hunter, or maybe just plain The Sterling Corporation. Get my drift? Well, so long, kiddo. Enjoy yourself, though you're going to make it hard on yourself every step of the way.'

'Water off a duck's back!' said Jaime, looking right back at him.

'You must like trouble,' Simon said unbelievingly, 'and I'm telling you, you'll get just that.'

'I know, but listen, Simon, it's not really clever to make threats.' Jaime's heart was racing and she felt sick inside. The trouble was, though she found it easy to fence with words, her relatives had the edge on her in every department. They were ruthless and wolfish and hard as steel chips. She was actually a fool to cross them, rushing into verbal combat when she couldn't even guess at the real weapons they might use against her. The only friend she had at Falconer was her grandfather, a man with a serious heart condition. She could never use him as her supreme weapon. One spasm of anger or retaliation on her behalf might kill him. All she could do was use him as a bluff. So heartless themselves, the family might consider her equally ruthless to gain her own ends.

It was with the greatest relief that she heard the front door slammed shut as if in a massive protest. Uncle Gerard was furious with her. He would have to be careful to avoid a bad migraine. In another half-hour, she would ring through and make an appointment to see Quinn. Her grandfather was no ordinary man. He had done many things that couldn't possibly have been right, but now he was old and sick to death, absolutely beyond touching. Quinn probably had very good reason to hate him, yet she was quite sure he didn't. Quinn's purpose was resolute. He was brilliant and super-efficient, thunderously formidable on occasions, but he wasn't cruel. Somehow he had managed to retain an element of pity for her grandfather. She had seen it in his eyes.

Jaime sat very still at the table, a strange pallor under her skin. She was sick and shaken, but she wasn't feeling the full effects even yet. A vivid picture of Quinn began to move behind her eyes. His sombre dark face was smiling, a light passing across it, softening his beautiful, well defined mouth, faultless white teeth, brilliant black eyes with silver points of light at the centre. She saw him very clearly. He might have been sitting opposite her, one lean brown hand reaching out to her. She relaxed her rigid spine and all at once she began to feel better.

CHAPTER FIVE

JAIME crossed the foyer of the Hunter Sterling Corporation Building, making for the nearest lift. She was right on time, though she had found it necessary to use her grandfather's name to get through the armada of telephonists, receptionists, and private secretaries that surrounded the Corporation's top executives in an elaborate defence system. It galled her that Jaime Gilmore had cut no ice, but it was imperative she see Quinn. As Sir Rolf Hunter's granddaughter she had found it wondrously easy to speak to him, but not so easy to see him. He was tied up all morning and told her very briskly that he would meet her for lunch. She had hung up swiftly, but even then he had beaten her to it. It only took her a moment to assimilate the fact Mr Quinn Sterling's office was synonymous with the Holy of Holies. To be able to see him at all was some small comfort.

By the time she reached the top floor, she found he was further buffered by an anteroom. His secretary, an immaculately groomed brunette in her late thirties, was busy on the phone, but she went through the usual pantomime of smiling and mouthing silently to Jaime to take a seat. After a moment she replaced the receiver and enquired warmly :

'Miss Gilmore?'

Jaime said that she was, aware that she was getting a most meticulous head-to-toe inspection for possible relay to the rest of the typing pool. It didn't make any difference, but still she didn't really like it. One was supposed to look only briefly, then away again, not this show of undivided attention. She decided to return this frank stare, then the secretary picked up the intercom phone and rang through to Quinn's office. Another minute and he was there, opening the door, no smiles but the same brilliant alertness, thanking 'Betty' and showing Jaime through to his office, pulling forward the nearest chair.

'I've just got to make one more call, then we'll go. How are you, you look a little pale?'

'I didn't aim to be,' Jaime said wryly. 'Make your call, Quinn, I'll admire your office. It's very, what's the word? ...'

'Impersonal?'

'Not at all. It's more like a home away from home. Very contemporary and tailored. Perhaps you could do with a few paintings on the walls.'

'See to it for me.' He was walking around to the other side of the huge custom-made mahogany desk with its crystal and chrome desk appointments, his dark face utterly preoccupied.

'Are you serious?' She couldn't tell at all.

'Yes.' He looked back at her, obviously having to transfer his concentration to her question. 'You can handle it, can't you?'

'Of course. What price range?'

'Round the two thousand five hundred dollar mark. No more. Abstracts. Concentrate on the young up and coming.'

'I should get into this myself!' Jaime said, smiling at the thought.

'Can you?'

'A few people have been kind enough to say I needed encouragement.'

'Notably not your father.'

'That idea had already taken root in my own mind. You didn't plant it.'

'Don't flash your eyes at me, Jaime. Perhaps he didn't relish the idea of competition from his own daughter, which is what he might have got!'

'Oh well,' she said guardedly, 'it's neither here nor there anyway. We were discussing your paintings. Leave it to me. It will be a great pleasure. More, *exciting*!'

'Good girl!' He picked up the phone and immediately tuned out on her. Very shrewd was Quinn, and he had only met her father the once. She studied his handsome, downbent, frowning face, heard him ask for a Mr Brian Donovan, then she turned slightly in her camel-coloured suede upholstered chair, giving her attention to the scale of the room and the size of the walls. It was a very large office, with a long sofa flanked by contemporary chrome and leather armchairs with a chrome and glass table in front of this seating arrangement, well away from the desk area with its opposite wall of mahogany cabinets which came about waist-high. The room would take, comfortably, two large canvases, one above the rust-coloured sofa, another above the long line of cabinets. A flood of natural light streamed in from the lightly curtained window wall at the back of the desk. She shouldn't have too much trouble with her selection, there were many brilliant young artists to choose from.

She was still deep in thought when Quinn finished his call. He marked his desk calendar, then looked across at her intent face for a moment. She looked a dream as usual, very young-sexy-chic, but she *was* pale, and a number of possible explanations occurred to him.

'How are you coping with the family?' he asked, without compunction.

'You've half guessed it.' She turned back to stare at him coolly. 'A fight all the way.'

'Then it's time to get you out from under their feet!'

'That's what I'm here to talk to you about.'

'What happened this morning specifically?' he asked. 'Why?'

'Jaime,' he said impatiently, 'you're the very picture of health, the spirit of youth if you like, but this morning you're so pale, I get no pleasure from commenting on the fact.'

'Damn you, Quinn,' she said a little breathlessly, 'you're making me feel unattractive.'

'That wasn't my idea. I'm nearly nerveless, you're so beautiful. Are you going to tell me, or do I have to wait for hours?'

'After lunch, maybe,' she promised.

'In that case, we'll go out!'

He stood up and came around the desk to her, his eyes going over her, the gently tailored little blazer suit, her new hair-style that made the most of her lush fall of hair; a kind of sophisticated pageboy, glossy and perfectly cut, just clear of her shoulders. At the moment, with her head down, it was swinging in a shining dramatic curtain over one cheek. He leaned forward and tilted her head up, holding it there.

'Hello, Jaime.'

'Hi, Quinn!'

'You sound about ten years old.'

'Can you really spare me the time?'

'No.'

With his hand under her chin she was forced to meet the gleaming mockery of his eyes. They spelled out a kind of breathless excitement, an element of danger for her, and she was beginning to react. There was nothing calm or ordinary about Quinn. He was a super-human and very hard to handle. In fact she was sure she couldn't handle him at all. 'I have a funny feeling you're trying to hypnotise me,' she said with a wavering intensity.

'No,' he said briefly.

'All right, go ahead.'

'Not here, Jaime.'

'Not anywhere! I won't surrender. Go on, laugh, but I tell you I mean it.'

'You look pretty intolerably pressured. Coming?'

'You know quite well I want to.'

He leaned forward and almost lifted her to her feet, and the worrying thing was he could make her tremble, her initial sensations beginning to multiply by the second. She tried to smile at him, but the veiled intensity was shining out of her eyes. It was unsuitable and ruinous, but Quinn Sterling was dangerously fascinating to her, and she communicated her feelings with a youthful lack of control.

'I thought I could see you without kissing you, but I can't!' he said with sardonic self-mockery.

'Why not?'

'To be honest I don't know. I don't always do things I want to do. You seem to be swaying my better judgment.'

'That's ridiculous.'

'Yes, isn't it?' He ran his hand down the side of her neck and she was shocked at the trail of fire it left. Jaime was trembling now and with certainty he knew it, his touch sealing them both off in a private world. There was no one in the whole building and she was committed irrevocably to letting him dictate this awesome excitement. She shook her head and her hair swirled about his hand.

'I'm not used to this, Quinn.'

'What's wrong with it?'

'We haven't a thing in common.'

'Put that out of your mind for all time. It simply doesn't apply!'

'Well, it doesn't strike me as a very good idea. We're business partners, remember?'

He greeted that with an involuntary, disturbingly attractive laugh. 'Would you do me a favour, Jaime?'

'What?'

'Just shut up. It won't be half as bad as you seem to expect.'

She recognised that herself with awful clarity, the blood tingling in her veins, his dark face going slightly out of focus as if she were a little drunk. If he touched her she would precisely melt. She felt so weak and yielding, it was really the time to pray, but what would she be praying about, when it was this she so ardently desired?

'You mean it, don't you?' she half-whispered.

'I'm afraid so.' There was laughter in his voice that was quickly banished as soon as his mouth touched her own. It seemed essential for them to draw together as closely as possible until Jaime wasn't even sure she could move away from him again. The pleasure and faint pain he was inflicting on her was exquisite, a hard and ravishing, brilliantly provoked sensuality. Her body couldn't lie. Her mouth couldn't lie and she was responding very naturally and quite passionately to his consummate skill, making a suicide of her vow of non-surrender, thirsting after this complex and fascinating man. His ability to arouse her was fantastic and it was also alarming, even if he released her abruptly as though unwilling to prolong these impossible moments.

When she opened her violet eyes he was studying her closely. 'It's all right, Jaime, it's all over.'

'I think I'll kill myself!' she said dramatically.

'I'd never let you. You wanted it, I wanted it. Now we'll go out and have lunch. I've booked a table at Carlo's.'

'It's crushingly expensive,' she warned.

'And what's that to do with you?'

'Nothing.'

'I believe you.'

'I just spoke out of my habitual thrift.'

'I know, but I'm paying the bill. Besides, the food's superb and it's very quiet. I hate noise and being stared at when I'm attempting to put a bite in my mouth.'

'I wonder you're not used to being stared at. It's only just this minute struck me, but you're a very handsome man. An hidalgo with black eyes and black hair and an easy accustomed arrogance.'

'Thank you, Jaime. I wasn't looking for a compliment.'

'You've got one.'

'As long as you mean it.'

They had fallen into their usual light banter and her heart began to slow its mad racing. For a few moments there, his personality had engulfed her completely, so much so that the touch and the scent of him still clung to her. Now he had switched roles again from the intensity of a lover who knew intimately the very texture of her skin, to a charmingly domineering, much-older-and-wiser-than-you-are mentor. This way, at least, she could control her own body and mind, not give herself over to the tormenting, dazzling Quinn Sterling.

At Carlo's, their host came forward beaming, clapped his hands together, and made pleasant conversation, showing them to one of the beautifully secluded alcoves upholstered in plush velvet; an aura of everything in the very best of taste, the linen crisp as snow, the flowers small and pretty and freshly picked, a paradise of a restaurant if one had the financial standing to pick up the bill. Jaime, on her own account, would never have ventured through the front door. The world of affluence was new to her and she was deeply suspicious of high prices.

The food, however, when it came, was so delicious, the wine list so illuminating, that her ever-present conscience about the world's starving millions was momentarily lulled. This was her opportunity to speak to Quinn, to have his night-black eyes touching her lightly, with such infinite skill to sway and excite. They weren't even through the Sydney rock oysters with a cold Chablis before she knew she was going to tell him everything, very clearly and sharply as though it was all happening right under his eyes.

He listened in complete silence with no prompting, and simply contented himself with getting all the facts and not firing her justifiable sense of anger and alarm.

'That's it!' she said when she had finished, her blue-violet eyes blazing in her small face.

He gave her an odd smile, laced with his own well-projected smouldering. 'Extraordinary, Jaime! I could almost enjoy your tale, if it weren't for the fact you're too young to suffer their enmity.'

That silvery flicker in the centre of his eyes frightened her. 'It might have been just a lot of hot air,' she ventured, seeking not to tone down her own perfectly accurate account.

'No, Jamie,' he said, deadly quiet, 'you'd be making the biggest mistake of your life if you thought that.'

'I don't really. Uncle Gerard looked as if he could cheerfully have choked me. At least he put a lot of effort into the impression.'

'And Simon?'

'I think Simon has plans for me.'

'How?'

'You said it yourself, cousins marry.'

'I think it's a dangerous practice myself.'

She shrugged. 'The lesser of two evils. They can't really put a weight around my neck and drop me into the harbour.'

He was looking at her with astonishing attention, so hard and alert that Jaime, unused to his boardroom face, found herself blinking. 'And I'll tell you why,' he said tersely, 'you're the jewel of the family, the very apple of your grandfather's eye. They're not going to shed many tears when he goes, but they don't dare risk angering him now. They could only stand to lose. You see, little Jaime, you're much too important a person.'

'That doesn't prevent them from firing away at me when Grandfather is out of sight.'

'No,' he said grimly. 'I must tell you I regard it as a measure of your courage that you're mentioning me at all.'

'They hate you,' she said simply. 'Perhaps more than they hate me.'

'I've worked hard enough for it!' he said, and smiled.

'They're not too happy with my silly ambitions either.'

'Which, incidentally, is what I really want to know about. Tell me, Jaime, are you still interested in becoming a career woman, which means working very hard?'

'I'm not a piece of prized porcelain!' she said, looking bewilderingly delicate and worthy of a glass case.

He seemed to think so too, for his faint look of tension relaxed. 'Yet that's exactly what your grandfather wants and expects of you. Your future is secure. You don't have to work at all.'

She stared at him a little helplessly as though he had withdrawn his support. 'Why are you talking like this?'

'You've had over a month of wealth and comfort. It's assuredly yours for life if you toe the line.'

She looked down at the small, perfect centre-piece, the intermingling soft pastel shades. 'It might sound absurd, but wealth and comfort aren't among my goals for life. By-products maybe, not even necessarily. The thing is, I'm no good at wasting my time and whatever talents I've got. I don't want to get up about ten and sit around the pool all day sunning myself until it's time to dress and go out for the night.'

'A lot of people would be glad to put up with it,' he observed dryly.

She glanced across at him sharply, her violet eyes electric. 'Is our deal off?'

He threw up his hands, his teeth dazzling white in his handsome dark face. 'Jaime, Jaime, the times I've seen that warring glance! You're like the old man, did you know that?'

'Oh, shut up!'

'You are!'

'What does that mean, I've lost an ally?'

'Just a sprinkling of his drive would take you to the top.'

'I asked you a simple question, Quinn Sterling, my friend or my enemy. Are you still with me?'

'That depends, Jaime, on what I get back!' he said, and his words weren't merely sounds but a series of shivering caresses.

Curiously her body was curving towards him. 'I know that doesn't mean what it sounds like,' she said, wondering again at his mysterious and absolute power.

'No, it doesn't!' he said crisply as though he had

just changed his mind. 'Such a pity you're not ten years older.'

'*Please*, Quinn!'

He thought for a moment, his face losing its expression of mockery finely edged with sensuality. It tautened into the exact world of big business. 'I'm not a fool, Jaime, and I don't entertain angels unawares. To answer your query, I'm with you all the way. By the sound of it I'll lose money if I'm not. I've even lined up premises for you, and a staff of three. Now I have your assurance you're ready to start work, I'll go ahead and register a company with a working capital of, say, twenty thousand dollars.'

'That's a lot of money!'

'It's not, but it will start you off. First we'll see how well you shoulder responsibility, then we'll think of expansion. I know you've got sensational legs and you'll have to use them, charging around with samples, seeing buyers, shops, boutiques, department stores, that kind of thing. I imagine you're going to make up a small collection—you might at this stage have to model them yourself. You'd be ideal.'

Her eyes were fixed on him, captivated with the whole idea, blazing with a youthful intensity to succeed. 'I have my designs already worked out. They're aimed at the young fashion-conscious with not a great deal of money. Someone like myself who likes to look good and can't spend a fortune. I'd prefer to do everything myself for a while. Detail is so important. What about this staff?'

'Excellent women, I'm sure. They're only too pleased to line their pockets at any rate. I'm sure you'll find you can delegate the assembly of the garments to them, but I'll leave you to handle all that. One of them is a graduate from the Institute of Technology. The other two, older women, have worked for various fashion houses. None of them have the verve or the flair to get going on their own, but they'll be just what you want in the way of a team. In time you can do the designing and the organisation of the cutting sheets and let them do the making up.'

Jaime picked up her wineglass and drained it, knowing she was being rash, but lured on to a wonderful new horizon. 'Where are the premises?' she asked.

'Double Bay.'

'Classy?'

'Sort of. A most agreeable place to start, anyway.'

'How am I going to thank you?' A surge of rapture was on her, colouring her flawless skin and flooding out of her eyes.

'*Succeed*,' he said, and resisted the strong impulse to give her quite a different answer.

'Oh, I will!' she promised, reaching over and touching the tips of his fingers.

'You're very brave in a restaurant.'

Their eyes met and the seconds spun out endlessly. 'Don't play games with me, Quinn.'

For answer he imprisoned her wrist.

'Tyrant!'

'Partner!' he said, watching her from under hooded lids.

The silence lengthened until a pulse began to beat at the base of her throat, a little frantically, and her thick black lashes fell on her cheeks. 'If you let me go I'll tell you something else.'

'I'm not hurting you,' he said.

'Yes, you are. It's strange, but you are.'

'No other way is possible, Jaime!'

'I knew the moment I laid eyes on you you'd affect my life,' she said inconsequently.

'I'm not demanding anything, am I?'

'You're a very clever and perceptive man, Quinn. Perhaps you're trapping me into something.'

'Keep that up and I really will hurt you.'

She lifted her head and saw his bitter, beautiful smile. 'I'm sorry.'

'I want to make love to you, Jaime. Now.'

'For everyone to see?' she said, with her own incurable desire.

'I thought we were on an island.'

'Would you then?'

'If you can say that you know nothing about me at all.'

Her hand under his trembled convulsively and he released her as though suddenly contrite or at least mindful of her youth and innocence. 'Relax, Jaime. These are only words. I won't lose track of the fact that you're only nineteen going on twenty.'

'An open book for you to read,' she agreed bitterly.

'I *am* hurting you, aren't I?'

'I told you that. Right at this minute you could lead me anywhere. I suppose that's because I'm a woman, but I'll grow up.'

'Stop it!' he said pretty forcefully, but quiet, 'or I'll abandon the rest of the afternoon just to see that you do.'

'I'd say no.'

'*You'd* say no! You said it yourself, Jaime, I could fashion you into anything I want.'

In her heart she knew this was true, and if it was true then she loved him. He was now an integral part of her. To have come so far in so short a time! One would have to believe Shakespeare. She had been marked out from the beginning to love Quinn Sterling. The tears came into her eyes, making them glitter like gemstones.

'Jaime!' he lingered over her name as though he loved her too, which was impossible. 'I swear if you cry, I'll just pick you up and walk out of here.'

'What about all these people?'

'They wouldn't stop me.'

'I don't suppose they would. I think I'm a little sick with you, Quinn,' she confessed with complete self-abandonment.

'Don't despair, you'll get over it.'

'Is it so obvious?'

'These things are always mutual, Jaime. Do you think I can forget the sweet taste of your mouth? I don't delude myself about things like that, but you're just a child starting out and I'm determined to give you a start. If you've got any sense at all you'll tell me your other news.'

'It's about Derry,' she said, trying to concentrate. 'I rang him the other night. May I have another glass of wine, Quinn?'

'No. Go on.' He relented slightly and half filled the tulip-shaped goblet. 'You speak of him as though you're the parent.'

'I have a very responsible nature.'

'Yes,' he considered. 'In a lot of ways you're very mature for your age.'

'But not mature enough?'

'I regret it as much as you do, but cradle-snatching isn't in my line.'

'Then I'll tell you about Derry. He has a showing coming up in December. He's well and he misses me, and he's getting married again.'

110

'Good God! I thought you said that would never happen?'

'I may be a lot simpler than I thought. In fact it looks very much like it. Derry has decided he can't do without household help, or so he told me, and he doesn't see me coming back.'

'Tavia?' he asked simply.

'I believed so myself, but no. Her name is Gayle and she's seven years older than I am.'

'Then you'll be delighted to meet her.'

'No,' she said firmly.

'Too much of a surprise?'

'It shouldn't be, but it is.'

Quinn regarded her for some little time. She looked faintly disconsolate and he felt an unaccustomed, betraying tenderness. Her hair fell like thick silk on to her shoulders and her small elegant features had a rare delicacy and strength intermingled. Perhaps it was the expression more than anything, the intelligence and character that shone from her eyes. She had appointed herself her father's keeper and she had taken the job seriously. Now she appeared to be blaming herself for her father's suspected aberration. His voice when he spoke was cool and impassive, on neither side.

'Your father is a very attractive man, Jaime. He has charm and talent. I'm sure he could have made more of a mark in the art world had he really tried.'

'I know he could,' Jaime said sadly, 'but he's incurably lazy.'

'Gayle might help there. I know you find it hard to comprehend, but sometimes a wife can accomplish far more than the most conscientious daughter. For example, Gayle may have a child. Raising a family takes money.'

'Not much was spent on me,' she pointed out.

111

'And you've done nicely enough without. Aren't you happy for him?'

'Of course I am! I just hope he's doing the right thing.'

'Naturally, but a young wife might be particularly pleasant.'

'What a pity he's not like you!' she said faintly caustically.

'Shame on you, Jaime!' he said solemnly. 'You scratch nicely when you're brushed up the wrong way.'

'It's ironical, though, isn't it?'

'It's life. Don't worry, Jaime, your father has always fallen on his feet and will continue to do so until the end of his days. Some people have that gift.'

'Then I'm happy, and I hope he makes Gayle happy too.'

'She does have the whip hand. She's young. Your father will put himself out to keep her.'

'If I was really honest I'd say I was a little hurt,' she admitted.

'Your honesty, Jaime, makes you a very interesting person. As well you're beautiful and you're generous. You'll attend your father's wedding happily. I'm only hoping for an invitation.'

'I'm sure you'll get one—he sent his kindest regards. None to Grandfather and not a mention of the rest of them. There's no love lost there.' She glanced up and caught sight of a small group of people coming into the restaurant. Two of them she knew. 'I thought you said this place was quiet?'

'And it isn't?'

'Leigh and a friend just came in. They're heading this way, quite unmindful of Carlo's directions.'

'A stroke of unlooked-for bad luck. Don't panic, Jaime. No one is going to attack you when I'm around.'

112

'Possibly, I wouldn't know. Leigh is kind of gone on you, isn't she?'

'A wreck.' His black eyes wandered over her. 'I've just had a brainwave. As a kind of cover would you consider getting engaged to me?'

'The best plan in the world!' she said absently, used to his amiable nonsense.

'When do you think we should announce it?'

'Why not now?'

'Right!' he said with rapier-sharp alertness, one black eyebrow lifting in appraisal. 'And I couldn't have chosen a more dazzling fiancée, a little on the young side, though I'd be the last man to hold such a child to her promise. Think of it as temporary protection for both of us.'

Something in his tone made her look away from the advancing party and right into his sparkling black eyes. 'Quinn?' she asked distractedly, her breath catching.

'Leave it to me,' he said firmly. 'I've got your very best interests at heart, not to mention my own. Ah, Leigh, Carolyn!' He stood up suavely, the most charming false smile on his chiselled mouth.

'Why, hello there!' Both girls stopped at the table, Leigh acknowledging her cousin with a gleaming gaze, Carolyn smiling, enjoying every moment. Both of them looked directly back at Quinn, intensely handsome with a magnetism no woman could fail to recognise. 'And what are you two doing here?' Leigh demanded, tossing her blonde head.

'*Shall* we?' Quinn asked, capturing Jaime's distracted gaze.

She sat there, speechless and completely unresolved. Had he gone mad? He had, for he began to explain himself to the two girls. 'Actually, Leigh, Carolyn, you interrupted an extremely tender moment. You know my fiancée. You must admit she's beautiful—and clever, which isn't strictly necessary.'

An earthquake couldn't have rocked them more. Leigh visibly lost colour, and her hand went to her throat as though her white jade pendant was choking her. 'You're joking!' she said, wildly in need of reassurance. 'I know how you like to throw people into an uproar!'

'Call it what you like,' he said pleasantly, 'but Jaime and I are unofficially engaged.'

'You can't possibly mean it.'

'The announcement will be made in a day or two.'

'*No!*'

'I'd say yes!' Carolyn contradicted her friend dryly.

'Have you told anyone else? Grandfather?' Leigh said desperately, a kind of venom creeping in.

'Not as yet,' Quinn answered for the unnaturally silent Jaime.

'You should have found out first if it was all right with him,' Leigh persisted.

'We'll call him later on and ask. Jaime, darling, I don't like to hurry you, but I'm due back at the office. We'll skip coffee if it's all right with you.'

'As long as you make it up to me this evening,' she managed, falling back on her experience with the school dramatic society.

'Harping already?' he responded. 'What a wife you'll make!'

Leigh couldn't smile, couldn't speak. And Jaime felt her heart move out in pity. She was genuinely sorry to see her cousin so stricken. None of this was really penetrating her own mind; Quinn was a skilled manipulator of people, but surely he didn't have to go to extremes? If he was setting a trap to catch her, she had fallen right in. On the other hand, it was reasonable to

114

believe that he was acting for the best. A fiancé was an acceptable guarantor in a business project.

They were all on their feet now, with Leigh looking like a witness to some appalling disaster, yet she kept doggedly on. 'I won't congratulate you,' she said in a throttled voice, her eyes on Quinn's face, 'because you're making a frightful mistake!'

'Please, Leigh!' Carolyn said, seizing her friend's hand.

'Do go on!' Quinn nodded his arrogant dark head, not in the least sorry for her.

Leigh responded, her lips scarcely moving, seeing and hearing no one but Quinn. 'You can't!' she said pathetically. 'It's not possible. You're up to something as usual. You spend your entire life trying to outflank and outmanoeuvre everyone.'

'Don't be absurd, Leigh,' he said dryly, 'I don't try. It really works.'

'My God, and you know how I feel about you!'

'Please, Leigh, no scenes here!' Carolyn begged. 'There are people we know here.'

'There could be millions for all I care!' Leigh threatened, her pale green eyes flaming.

'Perhaps,' Quinn said gently, 'your mother might. I can't see all that clearly, but two of her dearest friends are over there. You missed them on the way through.'

'*You* did this!' Leigh transferred her burning acid glance to Jaime, her face working.

'No, Leigh.'

'For heaven's sake,' Carolyn gritted, 'we aren't children. There's no need for a brawl.'

'Yes, and if you don't move Leigh along it would get worse,' Quinn warned her gently. 'It's strange, but I thought you would be pleased.'

Leigh's eyes were seeing him again and Carolyn suddenly got her hand under her friend's arm with such strength and determination that Leigh found herself being borne away against her will.

'What a pity!' Quinn murmured. 'I'd like to have heard the rest.' He took several notes from his wallet and placed them on the table, weighing the edges down with a bread and butter plate.

Jaime watched him, unable to match his poise but feeling she had to pass a remark. 'You're cruel!' she whispered.

'What was that?'

'I said you're cruel.'

'So I am,' he agreed brightly, taking her by the arm and steering her towards the door. 'I should have damned well got engaged to Leigh or even Sue. It just so happens I chanced on you.'

'You're insensitive,' she continued, low-voiced, staring straight in front of her. 'To choose this moment. You know she loves you.'

'Rubbish!' he said violently.

'Well, she thinks she does, and no one told her not to. It's unbelievable!'

He said nothing until they were well clear of the restaurant, the full sunshine beating down on their heads. Then he looked at her in a hard and controlled way. 'Stop acting like your cousin, Jaime, or I'll break off our engagement.'

'I can't see how you can,' she retaliated instantly. 'I'll sue you. Breach of promise.'

'That's my girl! That kind of thing is important.'

'It *has* to be!'

'It so happens I think we'll enjoy it.'

'And when it's all over?'

'You'll be a much better girl for it.'

'So *you* say!' she said dryly, her heart fluttering.

116

'Anyway, I think I know what's in your mind.'

'Do tell me,' he invited, and looked so easy and relaxed that she really wondered.

'I somehow fit into your plans,' she suggested rapidly. 'I mean, I'm useful to you.'

'I thought it was the other way round, but never mind. I certainly desire you, Jaime.'

'Not *that*!' she said, her head spinning. 'And don't you dare laugh. I feel giddy.'

'The wine. I did try to stop you. The thing is, I do need you, Jaime. You *do* fit into my plans and yes, I won't deny it. You're so shrewd you see through me.'

'And it was all premeditated?' she persisted.

'No, more of a spur-of-the-moment thing. For all we know you could head a multi-million dollar fashion house some time in the foreseeable future. That's what you want, isn't it? A fiancé seems a small price to pay.'

'I want to put Australia on the map,' she said with a glorious vision. 'I want to dress my own countrywomen superlatively well. Maybe our children too. I have great ideas for the kids as well.'

'Bravo! There you are, Jaime,' he said, resonantly congratulating her, 'and they don't call me a tycoon for nothing either. Why, a girl like you could go zoom to the top and I'm going to be there when you arrive.'

'And that's all there is to it?' She was so giddy that she couldn't for the life of her see how she would get home.

He smiled. 'Must we discuss this in broad daylight? I'm seeing you tonight, aren't I? I'll call at Falconer and confront the Old Man. The rest don't matter.'

'It should be an eventful evening,' she said vaguely. 'Just don't drink anything Sue-Ellen might pass you.'

'It's comical, isn't it?' he asked charmingly. 'Three beautiful girls all anxious to marry me.'

'Two,' she corrected sharply. 'I'm not marrying any-one for years yet. I'll be much too busy. I mightn't even marry at all.'

'I know exactly how you feel.' His tone was warm and sympathetic. 'Just don't leave it until that shining black hair turns a nondescript grey.'

'Not these days,' she said, reacting seriously. 'No one need put up with a single diabolical strand.'

'Just be quiet for a moment, would you? My own head is starting to whirl.' He was regarding her closely, then he suddenly caught her shoulders and almost turned her into his arms. 'By the time you get home you'll find the glad tidings have gone before you. Not all the angels are in heaven. I'll tell you what I'm going to do now. I'm going to drop you off at my unit and you can spend an hour or so there. You'll be quite alone and there should be plenty to interest you. No doubt you'll want to suggest a few telling changes, curtains and slip covers and so forth. Take a cab home at about four. I'll give you the money . . .'

'I don't want it!'

'Will you *be*? When you get there, just keep saying Quinn will be calling this evening. Got it?'

'Got it!' she said like an automaton. 'Quinn will be calling this evening. Where are we going, by the way?'

'Do I detect a definite pick-up of interest? I think we'll have dinner with Grandmamma. Rosemount isn't Falconer, but I like it a whole lot better.'

'Rosemount is beautiful.'

'My grandmother is content with it. She won't hear of any improvements or changes. The house speaks to her of the old days, happier times. I can't think of many myself.'

'Maybe you're neurotic?' she suggested.

'Oh, I love that!'

'A very smart neurotic, self-sufficient and secure, but complex nevertheless!' She looked at him, her beautiful thoughtful eyes on his face. 'Are you going to tell your grandmother of the master plan? I couldn't bear to deceive her or Grandfather. I've become very fond of him. He's my grandfather whatever he's done, and he's done a lot of good as well as pulling a few people down.'

'He has, you know.'

'Done a lot of good?'

'Forget it. Don't take any notice!' Quinn's face was intensely alive, darkly, vividly handsome, the sombre look completely dispelled. 'Surely you're content to be engaged to me for a while? I assure you I'll act the part.'

'The point is, I don't want you to!'

'You haven't yet mastered the outright lie. We do *not* propose to deceive anyone Jaime. We *are* getting engaged, and who knows, by the time you're ready to consider marriage I might have sufficient life in me to consider it myself. That way we won't break up what I'm sure will be a most promising and rewarding business relationship.'

His hand had fallen on her shoulder and she twisted her head up to him. 'You're an expert at this kind of thing.'

'Yes, I am. Anyway, Jaime, at this particular point of time, I don't think you could survive in the cruel world without me. I represent protection for the working girl, and believe me you need it. Your father is too far away and content to stay there and your grandfather is beginning to die right in front of our eyes. It's not necessary to mention your other relations. One other thing,' he said coolly, 'you may take it as gospel that I won't attempt to seduce you.'

'I couldn't be tempted,' she said, shocked so much that the words left her throat with a stammer.

'We'll debate that at a later date. Just when I'm ready to kiss that petal-smooth mouth.'

'A kiss is not consummation.'

'No, but can't you see where it could lead? Anyway, Jaime, we have an agreement.'

'Until it's broken,' she amended.

'I happen to want to stick to it. I swear I only wish to cherish and respect you, little Miss Teen.'

She gave a muffled little sound that could have been interpreted as outrage. 'I don't care a damn about that. I'm determined to match you.'

'Thank you, Jaime,' he drawled, his brilliant gaze very lazy and misleading.

'It wasn't a compliment.'

'Yes, it was. You know it was. You're half way to being in love with me already.'

'I must be if you say so.'

'Get in the car like a good girl,' he said crisply, 'I can't stand around talking nonsense all day. I'm like a general, I always have to be around for briefings!'

'You're brilliant!' she said, trying to bury her sparkling female antagonism.

'I expect you're quite right.' He almost pushed her into the car, and she had to clench the dashboard to prevent herself from hitting him.

'Come, come!' he said, and caught her fist. 'That's no way for a fiancée to act.'

'I'm wishing I'd denied it.'

'No chance of that!' he said softly. 'You're right up to your neck. Who else is there to back you in Just Jaime?'

'That's a great name!' she burst out involuntarily, her violet eyes dilating.

'And it's part of the deal.'

His dark face was very close to her and unconsciously

she brought up her hand and touched her mouth in concentration, as if the feel of his mouth was engraved upon it. It proved fatal, for he bent his head swiftly and covered her mouth with his own. 'Does that solve the mystery?'

Lights seemed to be dancing all around his head and she couldn't tell if she was showing the tumultuous shock of feeling she was experiencing. 'You scare me,' she said truthfully. 'I shouldn't have expected no strings to be attached.'

'That would have been too damned childish! Consider yourself engaged. Maybe I've been plotting to get you all along.'

'For God's sake, why?'

'Oh, come on now, Jaime!' His expression was hard and mocking and charming all at once and something else, and seeing it she quailed. Possessive. She would have to spend her time as his fiancée until he decided she was no longer necessary to his schemes. The only possible answer was to go home, but she wasn't going to do that. *Just Jaime* would be her distinguishing label. She too could have plans, and this arrogant, challenging, absolutely fatal man would lend her his tremendous vigour and organisational know-how.

She was filled with a remarkable energy, but managed to fall asleep at Quinn's very luxurious home unit that had a superb view of the harbour and the city lights by night. Because she felt generous Jaime had by then decided she couldn't change a thing, except maybe the repositioning of a Persian prayer mirror to the entrance foyer. Quinn had superb taste, and equally important, he was going to help her.

She couldn't scorn his offer to become engaged to her. He was a fantastic man and one couldn't expect such a man to be without complications. She didn't

CHAPTER SIX

THE first person Jaime saw when she got back to Falconer was Georgia. She swept down the staircase, her green eyes sharp enough to drill a hole through an unopened door, her voice icy with dignity.

'Your grandfather is waiting for you in the library,' she announced.

'Good for him.'

'You haven't a hope of pulling this off, you know that, don't you?'

'Pulling what off?' Jaime stalled.

'This phoney engagement!'

'What's it to do with you?'

'Everything!' Georgia maintained broadly. 'My daughter has been in love with Quinn Sterling for years!'

'Well, these things happen. I'm sorry for her, of course, but really Quinn doesn't feel that way about her.'

'What would you know about it?'

'Take my advice.'

'He's only using you!' Georgia said in a low voice.

'It's no good, Georgia; extraordinarily enough I don't mind.'

'You don't mind being used? How humiliating!' Georgia paused, trying to control her rising tone. 'You're not in trouble, are you?'

Jaime shook her head. 'What are you thinking of organising? No, Georgia, I leave trouble alone.'

'I was under the impression you were causing a great deal of it!'

'It's not a crime to get engaged, is it? Some people might wish me well!'

'I wish you the very reverse!'

Jaime looked at Georgia's handsome face curiously. 'Why? *Why* do you hate me? It seems mindless.'

'The fact remains you're trying to wreck this family. My daughter's happiness.'

Jaime sighed. 'Excuse me, won't you? You did say Grandfather was waiting.'

'And don't you dare upset him,' Georgia cried.

'Would you mind? I had the distinct impression you're all waiting for him to die!'

'You detestable creature!'

'Not detestable at all—smart. I also care about my grandfather, which you don't.'

'You just wait until my husband gets home!' Georgia said through her clenched teeth.

'Ring him,' advised Jaime crisply.

'I already have.'

'And who rang you? Leigh. She's in love with Quinn as well. It's almost like an epidemic.'

Georgia stared at her, her eyes glassy. 'You'll wish you never came to Falconer before I'm finished with you.'

'Lovely! Get out of my way, Georgia, I'm not going to stand here and swap insults with you. You have everything and it's not enough, and you've taught your children no better. You're a greedy, ugly woman!'

'I was a legend in my girlhood!' Georgia shouted, her throat flushing and her hand tearing at her caftan.

'I don't mean your looks,' Jaime said wearily. 'I mean the real you, inside. You know, where you live. You lack something vital—charity.'

'It's time we got rid of you!' Georgia said, stepping

nearer, a tall and a strong woman, three stone heavier than Jaime.

'Not a chance,' Jaime said breezily. 'I like mixing with the real élite. It's so ennobling!'

While Georgia paused to take breath, Jaime went quickly round her, and on to the library. It was a wonderful room, which housed a valuable collection of books in arcaded ceiling-high recesses. It also incorporated her grandfather's study, and the cedar tables and smaller cabinets held the trophies, the awards and the honours, the great pile-up of personal memorabilia her grandfather had accumulated during a long eventful lifetime. Rolf Hunter wasn't just one man but a number of men, and even his enemies acknowledged his confounded excellence.

Today he looked frailer than usual, his relatively unlined and tanned skin almost blanched. Jaime threw her handbag down on an armchair and went towards him, her hands outstretched. He took them and she bent over him to kiss his cheek. 'What's the problem?' she said in her habitual forthright way.

He looked at her without his customary enthusiasm. 'Georgia has been babbling endlessly to me about some engagement.'

'She had no right to do that.'

'She has some rights, Jaime,' he said forcefully.

'What are they? None so far as I'm concerned. You don't look very comfortable there at the desk, Grandfather. Come over to the sofa, then we can both sit down.'

'Perhaps I will, as I'm determined to continue this discussion.'

'You're not delighted?'

'It's true, then?' He shot her a baleful look from under his thick black brows.

125

'Sit down,' she said calmly, and waited for him to do so. 'Yes, it's true,' she murmured, sinking down beside him, 'but I wanted to tell you that myself. Quinn, in any case, is calling on you this evening.'

'Indeed?'

'I thought you admired him, Grandfather? You sent him to find me when you sent no one else.'

'You don't know Quinn, my darling.'

'Of course I don't. Do any of us know anyone? Tell me about him. Your view!'

'He's everything we do know. Brilliant, compelling, ambitious. He's the biggest persuader I know and he's willing and able to work superlatively hard. Actually he's been able to run rings around my sons for years now and he's only thirty-four now. There's no question he hasn't a great future, but he's deep. A very complicated man. For example, he's taking over my business right from under my nose. These days I'm content to sit by and watch human nature at work. I'm too old now to stop him and my sons wouldn't know how. I'm wondering now what his exact interest is in you?'

'Perhaps he loves me,' Jaime ventured.

He nodded. 'Of course. You're a very beautiful girl, yet still I wonder. It's not the money, it's not even the power. It's something else with Quinn. Family skeletons. They keep rattling. He'd use you if he had to.'

'As a matter of fact, Grandfather, he's helping me. I don't know if you notice my clothes?'

'Of course I do!' He looked at her in astonishment. 'What have your clothes to do with it? I must say I've wondered how you got the money to pay for them before you came here.'

'I made them.'

'One would never know!' He turned sideways to

126

stare at her, nibbling on his lip. 'It seems to me an expert couldn't do better.'

'I am an expert in my way,' she explained. 'At least I want to be!'

'Aren't we straying from the track?' he enquired.

'Not really. You see, I'm going into business.'

'You're *what*?' Matchless at taking shocks in his stride, he couldn't hide his objections.

'I'm like you, Grandfather!' Jaime said, trying to go carefully. 'Quinn only pointed that out to me today.'

'What kind of a business?' he demanded uneasily.

'Fashion. I want to design women's clothes.'

'Oh, really, Jaime!' he said impatiently, and somewhat relieved. 'It's not necessary for you to do anything. Enjoy your life!'

'I could only do that working. Surely you understand?'

'No, I don't!' he said sourly. 'It's a man's lot to work for the sum of his days, not a woman's.'

'Oh, Grandfather, you know very well that's not true any more.'

The handsome old face was glowering and one hand began to move jerkily. 'That's why women are so unhappy today. They don't know their place. They weren't unhappy in my day.'

'Perhaps they weren't allowed to say so,' she suggested. 'No one listened or cared!'

'I don't want to discuss it now, Jaime. Still, you mustn't think I'm not interested. Give yourself time. You love being here, don't you? You care about me. You can have anything you want—just name it. Not everyone finds work a pleasurable activity.'

'You did and so will I!'

'Forget that, Jaime!' he burst out irritably. 'You give me a long story about wanting to work when I want to

127

press on about Quinn. I don't like this engagement. You're much too young.'

'We're not rushing into anything, Grandfather.'

'It seems highly suspicious to me and knowing Quinn I'm right to be alarmed. Soon he'll have everything, including you. He idolised his uncle Nigel, did you know that? A very charming young man was Nigel. Charming but not practical. I never knew anyone who wasn't utterly taken with Nigel. He was a gentleman, the only one of them who wasn't a revolting aristocrat. He was lovable. Good—too good perhaps. I promoted the match between your mother and Nigel; he adored her, there was no other word for it, and he was prepared to extend the love that was in him to me. I've never known anyone else like him. Quinn isn't like him at all. He's more like his grandfather. Quinn can be as hard as nails. Nigel was too sensitive, too human, for his own good. I suppose you find it hard to comprehend?'

'No, his mother speaks of him in the same way.'

'Margo? She's always looked right through me, yet she loved Rowena. Between them, Rowena and Nigel, they nearly killed that old woman, but she managed to survive as I did. What Quinn has in mind I don't know, but be on your guard. He's going to be a great man one day, but I prefer him not to have my granddaughter.'

There was an intense, close look on Jaime's face. 'So you don't think he could love me for myself?'

'The human mind follows some pretty tortuous paths. You've looked into his black eyes, haven't you? They're fathomless. With you one can see right through to the soul. Paradise itself couldn't have a more heavenly blue. You're mismatched—Quinn is a very clever man, mature, and he's been around. You're just a child. You're courageous and gay, but that's nothing. I could give you the names of a dozen women who have flung themselves at his head, and that doesn't include my own granddaughters, spoilt silly little beggars. Things are complicated enough, Jaime, without your thinking of Quinn Sterling.'

'I didn't think about it, particularly, Grandfather. It just happened.'

'All right, I can understand that! God knows it's clear enough what you see in him, but break it off.'

'I'm not sure I can do that!' Jaime said strangely. 'I love him.'

'You're *in* love with him,' her grandfather pointed out heavily. 'Of course I know that. He's a handsome devil—they all were. And that's it. He's Philip's grandson. He looks at me sometimes with those probing black eyes and believe me I don't know who he is for a minute. But Philip was never ruthless; Quinn is, or he could be.'

Jaime nodded. 'All right, I can see you're serious and I can see that you're worried. I've come to love you, Grandfather, as though I've always lived here with you. I don't want to hurt and upset you. There's been enough hurt for all of us, but I love Quinn too. I promise you I don't consider that reason enough to marry, I won't rush into anything. You could be right. I know Quinn's a complicated man. If I said I didn't have doubts about him, I'd be lying. Time will tell. I'm going to become engaged to him for a while anyway. I might as well tell you the rest. He's willing to back me in a business.'

He caught her eyes steadily, looking tremendously alert. 'Has he gone into it?'

'You know Quinn.'

'Then you should be particularly proud of yourself.

Quinn doesn't back losers. Couldn't you have come to me? Why Quinn Sterling, for God's sake?'

'You've been ill, Grandfather, and you said it yourself, you're content to sit back these days, and that's as it should be!'

'Leave that part of it aside, if you don't mind. You should have came to me.'

'Would you have listened?' she enquired.

Unexpectedly he chuckled. 'Well ... not for some little while. Good grief, child, you've only just come back to me. The question of earning your own living doesn't arise. I've made millions, and I can't take it with me. I've left you secure for life. There's no law that says you've got to have a job as well.'

'We make our own rules, Grandfather. I'm a doer. I can't sit around and let someone else create and direct my environment. I think I have something to offer. I believe in myself. Didn't you believe in yourself?'

'I made Hunter Sterling what it is today.'

'Wasn't Philip Sterling entitled to some of the credit?' she asked.

'We're not talking about Philip Sterling, young lady. We're talking about his grandson, and let me inform you that Quinn is absolute in his intention to take us all over. Maybe he's getting back at me through you. You're the only weapon anyone could use against me. You're all I care about.'

She shut her eyes, her voice so quiet that he had to turn and look at her. 'How can you say that, Grandfather? What about Uncle Gerard, Uncle Vivian, my cousins?'

'You sound horrified,' he said, his eyes on her face.

'I am. Don't you care for them at all?'

'I suppose I should, but God damn it, I can't! Why should I? They don't care about me. They're all waiting for me to die as though they haven't got enough already. I've always been one-track and I suppose I'm not exactly an admirable person. I've loved my work, I loved my mother. I loved my daughter, and you're Rowena all over again. In a way I can't explain it's exactly like having a second chance. You've even a bit of me in you, I can see it myself. He's a shrewd devil, Quinn—diabolical. I've always recognised his perception. The only possible way he can hurt me is through you. The only way he can avenge his family is through you. I don't want you to marry him.'

'It may never come to that!' Jaime said, caught into this dilemma.

'Then why bother to get engaged? If you're serious about this business venture, I'll put up the money. Surely you know you had only to ask?'

'I do know it, Grandfather.'

'But I'm dying, is that it?'

'Don't say it!' She covered his mouth with her fingertips. 'Don't say it. With care you'll live for years yet! You'll see me make a success of myself. You won't see Quinn Sterling ruin my life. I won't let him!'

'Yet you love him?'

'If what I feel for him is real, yes.'

'It mightn't be enough,' he warned.

'Then we'll find out in time. I give you my solemn word I won't rush into marriage.'

'He has you plainly infatuated. I wish to God the boys were like him. Simon and Brett might make out— at the moment they're just nothing. They've had too much. Too much has been given to them and I'm to blame. I had nothing in my youth but conflict. No family. No money. I don't know how many jobs my poor mother and I held down to get me through university. I had a first-class brain, that helped. Philip

131

Sterling befriended me. The Sterlings, of course, were right out of the top drawer. Still, he was a good fellow. A brilliant engineer. Too moral, of course.'

'Can anyone be too moral?' Jaime asked, her eyes flying open.

'In business, yes.'

'You look calmer, Grandfather,' she said quietly. 'Do you feel it?'

He gazed at her thoughtfully with his steel-grey eyes. 'I can see you're not like your lunatic cousins, Sue-Ellen and Leigh. You won't let him make a fool of you. I couldn't drink the cup of bitterness again.'

'Talk to him tonight?' Jaime begged, and took her grandfather's hand, feeling the fine tremor in it.

'Yes, I will. We seem to be moving over the same old chessboard. You'll upset Margo, you know—a natural reaction. It's easy for you young people to talk about love; one is extremely lucky to know love and have it returned in a long lifetime. We're all beggars most of us, turned away from the table. Not even the crumbs. Still, I'm not infallible, it may be a splendid match. At the moment, however, that's not possible for me to admit. If he hurt you I'd kill him or have him killed.'

'Don't speak like that!' Jaime begged, frightened and with reason.

'What would you have me say?'

'I'm not so foolish or so weak that I need someone else to fight my battles. I mean it, Grandfather, I can handle Quinn, or I'll learn how to.'

He glanced away from her as though sick to death of the whole thing. 'It's child's play for a man to pretend he loves a woman. Stupid creatures, women, I've always found them so and I've had plenty of them in my time. A series of meaningless relationships.'

'That's the secret, Grandfather,' Jaime said, her

violet eyes saddened, 'one must be able to give love to receive it. To be prepared to suffer to gain much. You love me because you see my mother in me.'

'I see you in me as well. Why, damn you, I love you more than I loved Rowena. There, I've said it!'

Jaime glowed. 'You're not ashamed of it? You're not frightened to love me, to commit yourself?'

'I'm beginning to feel shame for a lot of things. That goes to show you how old I really am. All right, my darling, I can't pretend I'm joyous about this engagement, but I can play games as well as the next man, maybe even better than Quinn Sterling. I'm not dead yet. You're the prize and we both want you.'

'That's funny!'

'Very. A contested claim,' he said dryly.

'I love you both.'

'And if he doesn't love you, I ought to find out about it and I will. Yes, it's funny all right. History repeating itself, only I'm not handing you over.'

'When I came in you looked tired.' Defeated, she thought to herself but could never say. Now her grandfather looked vigorous.

'I'm not tired at all!' he said, supporting her.

'Good. I have a wonderful vision of you as a young man, tremendously handsome and alert. A real powerhouse. No wonder you understand Quinn.'

'Get me a drink,' he ordered.

'Are you allowed it?'

'Just one. Whisky with a little water. It's over there on the sideboard. What time is he coming?'

'We're having dinner at Rosemount, so it will be before then.'

'Good. I can't wait. He thinks he has an insurmountable advantage, but we'll see!'

'No tricks, Granddad!'

'I won't say. It's never been my policy to give away secrets.'

Jaime, busy pouring him a drink, glanced back over her shoulder and they both smiled. It wasn't until later that she began to be plagued with doubts. When it came to summing up his fellow man Rolf Hunter had never been far wrong, so regardless of her feelings she had to listen to his fears about Quinn. What did Quinn Sterling, with the world at his fingertips, want with her? She had said she could handle him. The difficulty would be doing it.

CHAPTER SEVEN

A MONTH later, the engagement still hadn't been made official, for Sir Rolf had found a very good reason to send his top executive and director to Japan for a series of important business talks. When he put himself out it was clear that Sir Rolf's word was still law. In any case their Japanese friends were showing considerable interest in Hunter Sterling Exploration and were pressing for the talks. It went without saying that Quinn was the right man to head the delegation and it didn't need Sir Rolf's firm assertion to convince Jaime that this was right. Uncle Gerard had gone as well, so she was spared his knife-edged remarks over breakfast. She had only seen Quinn once alone after that dinner at Rosemount. Her grandfather had been right about Margo Sterling's reception of their news; she had been shocked and genuinely worried, as though there was little chance such a match could come to fruition, let alone guarantee anyone any happiness.

Under the circumstances Jaime didn't find this attitude surprising, but Quinn had handled both of them with great charm and persuasiveness, talking most of the while about Jaime's plans and aims for her own company. At the end of the evening, Mrs Sterling hadn't seemed nearly so stricken, but it was obvious that never in her wildest dreams had she considered a marriage between them.

Jaime was the loveliest young creature she had ever seen, a more spirited, purposeful version of her mother, but a child still, one who had had no chance to mature, and in that Margo was wrong. Jaime's temperament, the events of her life, the solitude and frequent set-backs, had strengthened her backbone and decided her character. Jaime was a woman and she was able to cope with her new life far better than anyone imagined. Because she looked so young, so eager, so physically fragile, it didn't mean she hadn't learned how to survive and better, meet challenges. Quinn Sterling was the biggest challenge of her life, a frighteningly self-sufficient, self-assured man, but he couldn't force her into anything she didn't want. She was dedicated to making a success of herself, though she had to admit Quinn took her aspirations and burning ambitions quite calmly. She was no shrinking violet and if she wished to set the world on fire he was prepared and willing to help her. He had a great eye for talent in any field and considered it a precious commodity to be sponsored.

So brilliant and uncommonly successful himself, he would never fall into melancholia if he happened to marry a woman with a few grandiose ideas herself. Life would have to be exciting with Quinn, and there would be no room in it for a less than interesting life's part-ner. All the time he was away Jaime was so busy that she had to wonder how she found the time to miss him, but she did. Some vital part of her was a prisoner to Quinn; still she launched into her collection, involving herself with her team to such an extent that they were beginning to find words unnecessary, the same beautiful thoughts communicated through fabric and the feel of it, until finally Jaime was ready to show her small range to selected buyers. They had all expected it to be a series of triumphs, but it didn't work out that way.

By the time Jaime got back to the shop, she was so upset that she would have burst into tears, only she didn't have the energy. The collection that had sent Di and Marike and Jill into raptures had somehow looked terrible to three leading boutiques. The fourth, admittedly less exclusive, had found the garments attractive, in fact the buyer had just stopped herself from going into a rave in case she shot the price up. Anyway, she had placed an order. The rest had hated the entire range, but then they couldn't keep themselves from inspecting each garment very closely. There was something strange about the whole thing.

Jaime knew she was young and unknown and she had taken that into consideration, yet it was more like a planned refusal. 'The garments might sell anywhere else but here,' type of thing. The saleswoman at Claire's had changed her tune dramatically the moment the manageress declared her attitude. Up until then Jaime had almost chalked up an order. It didn't make sense. It was almost as if she was being undermined.

According to her team, and they were experienced, knowledgeable and very fashion-conscious women, Jaime's collection was a winner. They had greeted her designs with an overwhelming vote of confidence ready to follow her anywhere despite her youth and inexperience assuring her that the made-up garments would gain the *Just Jaime* label a reputation and lots of orders, perhaps make them all rich. Marike, a few years older, with a diploma in fashion design, was already a good friend and sincere admirer of Jaime's very adequately demonstrated gift. They had given her endless encouragement and she had let them run on, more than satisfied with their individual abilities, and already thought of them as important to her and was pleased to be able to repay them for giving of their very best. It was then more of a shock to learn that at least three buyers took the extreme view. Such a dismal collection wouldn't even go over in Siberia.

With the inbuilt conviction of the truly gifted, the

confidence in the face of severe criticism, Jaime found herself more sick and puzzled than disheartened. Her garments were far better made than most that were selling well in the stores, potential winners. Too bad they weren't going over.

She was so tired, so footsore, that she almost dragged herself through the showroom to the workroom beyond. In just on a month she had lost weight, so that every contour of her face and body appeared so much more delicate. She had even resorted to multi-vitamin pills, something she had never done before. It was past five, yet all three were waiting for her as if it was an occasion. One look at her face told the tale.

'I don't believe it!' said Di, always the spokeswoman.

'Me neither!' from Jill.

'What happened?' Marike asked, slightly annoyed with Di and Jill.

'Nobody was buying. Oh yes, Ultra Chic placed an order. A good one. The other three, Sally K., Dina's and Claire's, found the whole range upsetting. Brilliantly put together, the whole lot of them nearly took the garments apart, but they wouldn't consider selling them.'

'Sit down!' Di urged. 'If you get any skinnier you won't be able to model them.'

'You're not happy about something?' Marike persisted.

'No.' Jaime's blue-violet eyes were thoughtful. 'Maybe it's a weird idea, but I think we're being got at.'

'Who would do a thing like that?' Jill moaned, striving stoically to think of someone.

'What about your dear aunty?' Di suggested. 'I know for a fact she could make or break a few of the very exclusive boutiques. You won't trade on your name . . .'

'No, I won't!' This emphatically from Jaime.

'Don't get uptight, dear,' Di said soothingly. 'I'm only suggesting a possible line of sabotage.'

'And you could be right. I've heard about such things. In which case how do we go about setting things right?'

'Listen, my dear,' Di said with sublime confidence, 'the range is superb. You're a very talented girl and we're pretty cunning ourselves. Would you like me to put the word out on the streets?'

'What word?' Jaime asked rather wistfully, accepting a cup of coffee from Marike's kind hands.

'Who you are, dear!' Di said patiently.

'I'm Jaime Gilmore. Just Jaime.'

'And you can guarantee your dear aunty told them just that. No mention that you're Sir Rolf Hunter's granddaughter or anything like that.'

'If she was trying to stop me she'd certainly keep it quiet. Don't worry, Di, we can do without them. Their prices are too high anyway. I saw an imported rag on a model for six hundred dollars. Those kind of prices would destroy my very aim!'

'Be that as it may, with your talent the customers will pay. Let me drop a fact or two in a few pertinent ears. One doesn't like to trade on a name, but everybody does it.'

'I'm going to trade on my own ability—at least until I'm quite desperate,' said Jaime. 'Let me line up the department stores. Georgia can't buy them, or can she?'

'She's a very influential woman, which as you all know counts in this rotten world!'

'Well, it's Friday and well past knocking-off time. Monday I'll be ready to come back fighting!'

'Atta girl! The first step or two is pretty hard,' Di said fondly. 'I've been closely associated with this game for twenty years now. It's no secret that contacts are important. If I were you, young lady, even allowing for the fact that you have a genius for design, I'd get that beautiful face into the glossies as Sir Rolf Hunter's granddaughter, starting out in her own business. The implications are enormous.'

'I'll never get the Communist vote!' Jaime said, and laughed for the first time that day. 'I don't like it, Di. I want to make it on my own!'

'You very nearly didn't today, thanks to your aunt.'

'We're only assuming Georgia had anything to do with it,' Jaime reminded her.

'You did tell me Sue-Ellen had your design sheets on purpose!' Marike pointed out, her piquant face disliking the idea but not rejecting it.

'So she did.'

'Then I don't think there can be any doubt about it.'

'Maybe not!' Wearily, Jaime brushed her hand across her eyes. 'I never think when I'm as tired as this. Let's all go home.'

'Just you remember we're right here behind you.'

'Thanks, Di.'

'Shall I lock up for you?' Marike asked.

'Gosh, I forgot to tell you, Mike is waiting outside!' Jaime swept to her feet trying to look as if she was capable of locking up her own premises. 'All of you, thanks for everything, I'll reward you in time—now get out of here and have a nice weekend. Jill, take those flowers, they were only fresh this morning. Tell your mother they're a present from me.'

'Gee, thanks! Usually we have a few nice little daisies, not these beauties. How can you afford them?'

'I didn't,' said Jaime. 'They were sent to me—a persistent admirer. That's the second lot this week.'

'I wish someone would send them to me!'

'Why, bless your heart, they will. On your next

birthday.' Di rustled up a few sheets of tissue paper and wrapped the masses of beautiful carnations, presenting them to the very pleased Jill. 'See you, Jaime. Take care now.'

Jaime smiled and waved them all off, pretending an energy she didn't feel. For the first time it occurred to her that one could be dedicated and still feel terrible. The last month had taken a lot out of her, though she had been wondrously happy and fulfilled from time to time. This was possibly the aftermath. It happened, the unresolved tensions. She didn't want to, but she immediately thought of Quinn. She had wanted to please him with a full report of some modest success, but not after a day like this. If there was some plot going against her it was clear it had worked. Well, what had she expected, miracles? Ultra Chic were largely taken with the range; it was a start. On Monday she had two appointments with the leading department stores. She had to look forward.

At that moment she only succeeded in looking impossibly overworked, very young and dangerously fragile. She rested her elbows on the cutting table and looked away out of the window. There was no view to speak of, not the magnificent harbour vistas of Falconer.

Her grandfather didn't wish her to pursue this career of hers. Was it possible he was making things hard for her in the mistaken belief that she would fall back on him alone? He was capable of anything to suit his own ends. He harped constantly on the way she was cooped up in a workroom instead of being out in the sunshine enjoying herself. Sue-Ellen had the most glorious tan from hours in the pool or the surf. Jaime in a month had lost her pale golden tan to a clear ivory. It only served to accentuate her increasing delicacy.

Her chin in her hands, she considered her grandfather's remarkable record of interference and intrigue. He could force her out of business if he wanted to. He had become extremely possessive and jealous of her ambitions that denied him her time. Sabotage, every way she turned. Georgia wouldn't hesitate to injure her in any way she could. What few moments they had had together hadn't been pleasant. Sue-Ellen and Leigh were livid, mutually supporting, in their open contempt and rage over her supposed engagement to Quinn.

One month and still not a word from him. He was real and he was powerful and he would want to know how she had slipped up. At least he supported her, or did he? If she couldn't trust Quinn, she couldn't trust anyone. He was too big a man to crush a mere girl, non-starter in the power stakes. She let her head slide down on to her hands, shutting her eyes. She wasn't looking forward to the weekend. The only peace she could find these days was at Rosemount. It was very easy to talk to Quinn's grandmother; she was a highly cultivated woman, and her fashion judgment even for the young sophisticates was perfectly sound. It wasn't even necessary to explain things to her, and importantly she had given her sincere seal of approval to the Just Jaime collection. If she didn't move soon she would fall asleep at the table . . .

Quinn, leaving his parked car, saw Diane Collins waving frantically from the window of a parked car across the street. He walked across to her without hesitation, though he was anxious to see Jaime.

'How goes it, Mr Sterling?'

'Fine, Di, and you? How are you, Jill, I didn't see you there.' He bent his tall, lean frame to look into the car. 'How's Jaime?'

'The girl genius. You said it for us. We'll go ahead and repeat it.'

'That means she's got your approval.'

Di smiled. 'Not a single complaint. She's working too hard, and there's precious little of her. Apart from that we want you to know you let us in on a good thing. I've been in the business twenty years, and seriously, Jaime makes it all worth while.'

'Can I repeat that, please?'

'You sure can. We won't hold you up, we just wanted to say hello!'

'I'm glad you did. Jaime still inside?'

'The last one as usual.'

'I'll see she's through. When this collection's launched we'll have a party.'

'How's Tokyo?' Jill asked, smiling.

'Worth every minute, but it's good to be home.'

'You look like a man who got results.'

'Thank you, Di.' He smiled at her and for a moment Di had to support herself in the seat. Never, even in her early days, could a man drive her nuts, but then she'd never met a man like Quinn Sterling and he wouldn't have looked at her. Still, the smile was nice, like a sweet shudder up the spine. She nodded to the equally smitten Jill to start up the car, and with many waves and smiles they were off to the weekend routine. Work was more interesting these days and a party was something to look forward to. If Quinn had promised them one, he would stick to it. Both women automatically began thinking about what they could wear. Perhaps Jaime might dream them up a design. They just flowed out of her in an unquenchable stream, and she knew exactly how to hide figure faults.

Quinn looked around the tastefully decorated showroom, then walked through to the workroom, a slight

frown on his face. He was just about to call out:
'Jaime!' when he saw her.

Not the vibrant young beauty he had left with a
passion to conquer the fashion world, but an exhausted
young creature, her glossy black hair spilling around
her in silky confusion, the only side of her face visible
newly pale, without any colour whatever, a gleaming
ivory. Her thick black lashes and delicate arching brows
made up this black and white etching, for her vividly
blue eyes were closed. She looked so vulnerable, so
utterly spent, that he felt a quick surge of exasperation.
It was all very well to make her mark, but she didn't
have to make it in a month. That just proved what a
child she was!

'Jaime!' he said crisply, with a faint anger.

She didn't answer.

He went around the table and shook her, expecting
instant arousal. She had to be very tired, for she didn't
spring to life, but tilted her head back very drowsily,
her violet eyes opening, flower-fresh but still immersed
in some fantastic world of her own.

'Jaime!' he said again, his hand sliding down over
her back and closing at her too slender waist. 'Wake
up!'

'Quinn!' she said in a hushed voice, her gaze now
trapped by the sight of him, the warm strength of his
hand. 'What are you doing here? We didn't expect you
until next week.'

'Your grandfather knew perfectly well when I would
be home.'

'He never told me. Worse, *you* never told me.'

'Did you really want to know?'

'Oh yes!' she said unguardedly. The sight of him
seemed to be twisting her heart over. She wanted to
tell him he had haunted her subconscious, except for

144

certain times at night when she ruthlessly had to eject the conscious thought of him from her bed, but she was far from being in control of herself. The sight of him was so unexpected that he might well have been part of her dream. Her deep exhaustion, perversely, was unintentionally provocative. She was half lying back against him, her eyes resting with tantalising softness on each separate feature of his face. 'Hello, I missed you.'

'You say that very easily.'

'It's true.'

'Wake up, Jaime,' he said, moving to lean back against the table. 'You look unbearably desirable.'

'More so than the geishas?'

'Now how would *I* know?'

'You have a very worldly air.'

'Jaime darling, when in Tokyo, I'm totally committed to business.'

'And here?'

There were diamond points of light in his jet-black eyes. 'Do you mean to be so provocative, Jaime?'

'You're my fiancé, aren't you?' she asked with mischief. 'You said you were going to act the part very suitably.'

'Did I say that? I'm *not*. You don't look fit enough for a little sweet violence. Perhaps later on tonight.'

'I think you should kiss me now,' she said plaintively. 'I've had an awful day.'

'I can see that!' I'm ravenous myself, but I can wait. Right now, I'm going to take you home.'

She stretched her arms luxuriously above her head, arching the slender creamy column of her throat. 'I could do with a nice, scented, time-wasting, relaxing bubble bath!'

'Don't say another word!' he said dryly, 'I have to

draw in my breath just thinking about it. Stand up, Jaime, and let me have a look at you. You seem to have shrunk.'

'What there is is real. I seem to be aching for you in some odd way.'

'You shouldn't talk like that,' he warned. 'It's dangerous.'

'Why?'

'Why? Surely you know, Jaime. You don't have to plead to be made love to!'

'Then why don't you?' she asked with a strange insistence.

'You're in too much of a hurry. I'm taking you home.'

'All right, I won't ask again!' she said haughtily. 'I'm so tired I don't even know what I'm saying. In fact I'm not even properly awake.'

'Don't give up hope!' he taunted her, steadying her swaying figure.

'Keep your kisses for ever, Quinn Sterling. I don't want them.'

'Yes, you do. Fiercely!'

'But then you're so conceited,' she riposted.

'Very neat, Jaime, but it's not true. Come here. No tricks, I just want to look at you.'

She stood up straight and held up her head. 'Well?'

'Quite possibly you're even more beautiful. That's odd. Are you sure you want that badly to be a success?'

'What's success, for God's sake?' She really was swaying and he caught her shoulders and drew her gently against him, making no attempt to lower his head. 'I think I might have to carry you. You might have warned me you haven't shoes on. Your height shocks me. I'll pick you up about eight—that will give you a little time to sleep in your own bed. Anywhere else would just add to our dilemmas. You're doing quite enough of that.'

'I'm not!' she murmured, deciding to stay where she was for the duration.

'You know you are!' He suddenly swept her off her feet, cradling her lightly. 'God, Jaime, you're no weight at all, but at least you have some shape left.'

'Don't look at me like that,' she said drowsily.

'Why not?'

'I think you're only pretending about those geishas.'

'I have an ivory-skinned geisha of my own. What happened to that Gold Coast tan?'

'Ask Grandfather. He's very resentful of the time I've been spending away from him.'

'I know, I spent over an hour at Falconer. This will be my second trip today. He's very shaky, the Old Man, very frail. It seems to have happened overnight. It hurts me in a way to see him so diminished. You can't imagine what he was like.'

'Yes, I can. Grandfather thinks you're trying to hurt him through me.'

'How is that?' he asked sharply.

'You're hurting me, Quinn.'

'You deserve it.'

She linked her arms around his neck to balance herself. 'Are we still going ahead with this engagement?'

'More than ever. You fascinate me, Jaime.'

'There are shadows around you, Quinn,' she said a little sadly. 'Don't think I can't see them.'

His expression changed from a sensuous charm to a dark arrogance. 'Who's been talking to you?'

'*Everyone*. No one, including your grandmother, thinks I'd make you a suitable bride.'

'How mistaken can they get, when in fact, in some

147

ways I find you flawless. Satiny skin, violet eyes, black shiny mane, even that condescending little smile. I might as well kiss you at that.'

'Oh no, you won't,' she said, struggling so wildly he dropped her to her feet. 'I'm myself again.'

'Well, make sure you stay that way. You couldn't decide who you were a few moments ago. I would have thought you were mine.'

'It's better and wiser that I be myself!'

'Where would you like to go tonight?' he asked, his eyes searching her face with a turbulent brilliance.

'Oh, let's just go for a drive.'

This for some reason started him laughing, such a warm, disturbing sound that Jaime turned to stare at him with surprise, then a terrible suspicion. 'On second thoughts, we'll stick with the bright lights.'

'But, Jaime,' he said lightly, 'I promise you I'll treat you like a hideous, well-loved great-aunt.'

'Have you a great-aunt?'

'I had one until recently. I believe she was a glorious beauty in her day.'

'I'm not surprised. Being hideous isn't one of the Sterling misfortunes. You look remarkably well after your long trip.'

'And you look extremely touching just coming up to my heart, but collect your things. It doesn't pay to push yourself to the limit and I don't think you can stand up much longer.'

The room seemed to be swimming around her and her eyes looked dreamy and bemused. 'I don't seem to be asking you any of the important things. How was the trip?'

'Extremely successful, thank you, Jaime.' He moved over and checked on the windows. 'A deal has been arranged with very favourable terms for us. We have a few more talks with the government, then we can go ahead. I might ask you the same question. How's Just Jaime?'

'I'm not ready to talk about it,' she said, drooping disconsolately and letting him complete his circuit of the premises.

'Then we can easily talk about it tomorrow or the next day. I didn't expect you to wear yourself to the bone.'

'But I've been full of enthusiasm!' she said urgently. 'Everything was going so right, yet today three potential buyers knocked me back. It wasn't what I expected. The girls were pretty impressed and they don't impress all that easily, especially Di.'

'What buyers?' He came back and looked straight at her, a bracing look that made her pay attention. 'Give me a list of them. It sounds as if it could be a little elementary or crude blackmail, in which case you're far from sunk. Your grandfather is sour on the whole thing; ferocious, but kindly disposed towards you. I told you, remember, he wouldn't want you to work at all.'

'Damn you, Quinn, it was to *you* I came for help. I'm a lot smarter than you give me credit for.'

'And I'm glad of it. One little problem you can't thrash out by yourself: when are we going to celebrate our engagement? The Old Man has put us off long enough.'

He was focusing all his attention on her and Jaime reacted with a young girl's uncertainty. 'Talk to me, Quinn. You don't really talk to me. You don't even send me a postcard.'

'No time, but I remembered you. You have the right skin for pearls. A swan's neck. Stop staring at me.'

'Surely you don't think Grandfather is behind it?'

He shook his head. 'No, he's gone quite soft on you.

I'm sure it's making the family envious.'

'You're on my side, aren't you?'

'Indeed I am.'

'I wish I could be sure of it,' she sighed.

'You damned well should be!' he said tersely.

'Well, I'm not. I'm vaguely uneasy about you, Quinn. Your motivations.'

'Oh, be fair!' he said lazily. 'I'm merely trying to protect you.'

'It has to be that. I can't flatter myself you've fallen madly in love with me.'

'I told you—mutual protection. I'm tired of being chased by panting females and I'd feel quite safe with you. At least you've given me your solemn promise not to consider marriage for years yet, if at all.'

'And what's wrong with that, you mocking man?'

'Nothing. Let us say at once I'm taking refuge behind your stance. This way we can have the best of both worlds.'

'Don't make *that* mistake!' she said, swiftly gathering up her things.

'It was just a thought.' He came after her and turned off the light. 'It might save us from boredom.'

Jaime turned pensively, her head still tilted, her eyes an indescribable mixture of blue and hyacinth. 'I'm never sure if I understand you or not.'

'And I'm never sure the exact colour your eyes are. Did you ever consider I might be serious?'

'No.'

'All right, then! Let's check my intentions. I'm just your backer-advisor-sometime-protector. Valued, I hope. I wouldn't want you to think of me any other way. Is that the key you're hiding?'

'Yes.'

'Give it to me. Now I'm going to try and get you out

to the car. You look like a child who ought to be picked up and tucked into bed.'

'So you keep telling me. I must look pathetic.'

'No, you're terribly attractive to me as you must know. But I have this unshakeable grievance against cradle-snatchers. I've talked to you about it before.'

They were out in the street now, and she lifted her face urgently. 'I'm twenty. In another year I'll be twenty-one. Then what?'

'We'll talk about it then. I'm not prepared to act until you're at least thirty. Does that please you?'

'Indeed yes! I expect you'll be married yourself by then.'

Quinn steered her towards the car, then leaned forward and opened the passenger side. 'She'd have to be pretty exceptional. I haven't had the faintest urge up until now.'

'Nobody worthy?' she enquired.

'Nobody pleasant enough. You're a little cat yourself. Hop in and curl up.'

'Of course!' she replied sweetly, and instantly complied, settling back and crossing her long slender legs. She never quite knew what was happening to her when Quinn was about, but he made her come frantically alive. Her skin was electric with an unbearable sweet tension, an enormous excitement that made her feel giddy like a deep draught of mountain air recklessly taken and held.

Quinn got in beside her and gave her an odd, considering little smile, a combination of tenderness and taunting. 'Tell me what you're thinking about this minute?'

'No. I refuse to indulge you.' Her heart was beginning to drum wildly and she turned her head to look out of the window.

'All right,' he said easily, 'but don't think you can lock up your thoughts. I can see right through to your soul.'

'Then obviously I'll have to keep staring out of the window.'

'You'll turn to me of your own accord. I can wait!' He switched on the ignition and the big car purred into life. They crawled out of the narrow street until they turned on to the main road, then they picked up speed. It was a powerful and very expensive car and it was deeply comfortable so that after a minute Jaime relaxed her rigid spine.

Quinn glanced at her briefly and laughed. Her blue-violet eyes seemed to be imploring him, revealing and very beautiful. He put out a hand and lightly touched her cheek then he gave his total attention to the road. Jaime, totally relaxing still, didn't delude herself. There was no escape from Quinn, for wasn't she his latest acquisition?

CHAPTER EIGHT

FALCONER was a blaze of lights and Vivian Hunter's car stood in the drive some little distance from the gold Mercedes belonging to 'Robby' Burnett, Sir Rolf's close friend and personal physician for over twenty years.

'Something's wrong!' Jaime said with the first dreadful premonition.

'It may not be anything, Jaime. Try to keep calm.' Quinn swung the car round to the base of the stairs, his dark face inscrutable, but Jaime barely waited for it to come to a complete halt before throwing open the door and jumping out. All her senses were working overtime. The doctor's car alone seemed an unbearable menace. Quinn came round to her and grabbed her arm, restraining her, but already his sombre dark face was revealing his own forewarnings. 'We'll go quietly, Jaime. You mustn't lose control. Your grandfather was quite all right this afternoon. In fact, he was the best I've seen him for a long time.'

'He wouldn't be proof against another heart attack.'

'We'll go in,' Quinn said quietly. 'Your Uncle Vivian is here.' That in itself argued a relapse, but he didn't mention it. Jaime's desperate young face was hurting him.

'He could be dead!' she whispered, visibly trembling.

'The end has to come!' he said rather harshly. 'It was a miracle he rallied the last time.'

'I think my heart will break!' She was gasping, her eyes filled with tears.

153

His arm came round her shoulders, the fingers biting into her skin. 'You feel everything so intensely, Jaime. Your grandfather isn't afraid to die. He's very tired. I think he only wished to live long enough to see you.'

'I don't want him to die.'

'There's an end for all of us, Jaime, and we have to be prepared for it. Come, you're not alone!'

They found the entrance hall brilliantly lit and beyond they could see into the drawing room where the family was assembled. Everyone looked mortally stricken; whether by the threat of death and its bitter promise for all of them, or now, at the end, a sense of family and respect.

Gerard Hunter was standing in front of the fireplace and he turned his head towards them. 'My father has had another heart attack. He's not expected to live the hour.'

'Can I go up to him?' Jaime cried, in a frenzy of distress.

'No, Jaime, you cannot! I think you've caused quite enough harm already.'

She almost reeled, but there was more.

'You think you're one of us, but you're not!' he continued dully. 'My father wouldn't wish to see you.'

With her quick nervous recoil against Quinn's shoulder she could feel the icy rage in him and she knew without looking at him his black eyes would be glittering. 'Spare her your poison,' he said in a low, cutting voice. 'Jaime has given your father the only pleasure he's known in long years!'

'Please, Quinn!'

Both men ignored her. 'I would expect you to take that view, Sterling!' Vivian Hunter said sneeringly, but his heavy handsome face flushed a dark red.

'I haven't the brutality to be more honest at this time!'

Georgia, seated behind her husband in an armchair, suddenly began to moan helplessly. 'Must we make things worse? Have a care, Gerard. We may all be disinherited for all I know. Grandfather is much too far gone to see you, Jaime, and it would only distress you to see him.'

'I'd like to go up.'

'No.' Georgia buried her head in her hands. She looked genuinely besieged with anguish, overwhelmed by the thought of her father-in-law's imminent death. He had always been there, manipulating their lives. It didn't seem possible that he could be human enough to die. She was suffering from a guilty conscience as well, for she had been out all day and she had often wished him dead of late. It was puzzling now that she could be so truly torn.

Vivian Hunter, at the head of his family group, stood nibbling his luxuriant moustache, the only thing that marked him from his brother to the casual eye. He was determined now not to fall out with anyone. He was discovering too for the first time in years that he loved his father—more, worshipped him for the financial giant he was. Not that his father had ever loved him, and with a kind of deeply driven sense of inferiority he had learned not to expect it. It was now an added punishment that he had seen so little of the old man of late. The years since his boyhood were flashing past his eyes at a frantic pace, his father dominating every one of them. Now he was going, perhaps gone, an old man with nowhere to conquer. A giant no more. Evelyn, his wife, was crying quietly and he patted her shoulder, the first time he had done that in years. She didn't draw away, which was unusual, but rather seemed to be comforted by it so he continued in this mellow, melancholy vein.

Robby Burnett was suddenly in the midst of them, scanning their faces. 'The position is grave. He's conscious, but not for long. Jaime, would you come up? Quinn, you might come with her.'

'It doesn't really matter about the rest of us, does it?' Gerard Hunter called bitterly.

'I'll call you all in a moment!' Robby merely replied. 'It's Jaime he wants to see, and she'll need somebody. None of you seems to qualify.'

The doctor turned away, his eyes flashing. He was infinitely upset himself and finding it difficult to hide. Rolf Hunter had been his closest friend and a brilliant mind. He knew perfectly well what a lot of people said about him, and he even believed some of it, but Rolf was his friend to the death. Rolf's sons he had never liked, but they had suffered on their father's account, terribly perhaps, and this thought made him turn back and lift his hand to them as though exonerating their sins.

'Pompous old goat!' Sue-Ellen hissed when he was out of earshot.

'He is your grandfather's friend!' Georgia pointed out severely, still feeling virtuous.

'Yes, and so is Jaime. I think we should all be worried.'

'*I* am!' Gerard Hunter maintained heavily, beginning to pace up and down.

'Didn't Father ever reveal to you the contents of his will?'

'No, he didn't!' Gerard suddenly roared, rounding on his brother.

'Well, we'll never be exactly broke!'

'You've always been a fool, Viv!'

156

'Yes, that's so!'

'Don't agree with him, Dad,' Brett protested. 'Stick up for yourself!' he admonished, emerging as his father's protector.

'Shut up!' his uncle said cruelly. 'When we want to hear from you we'll be dead ourselves.'

Brett muttered something unprintable and Sue-Ellen gracefully collapsed into the armchair opposite her mother. 'This is marvellous, isn't it, and so typical! We sit here feuding while Jaime grabs the lot!'

Her mother was coming out of her reluctant trauma. 'Oh, for God's sake, Sue!'

'Oh, don't persist with the act, Mother. We all knew this was going to happen. Old Robby warned us ages ago.'

'You're so young and so terribly cynical!' her mother wailed tearfully. 'I don't even think I like you.'

'On the other hand, this tearful mood will pass. I'm sorry Grandfather is dying. I really am. Please note that I don't wish to go up to the sickroom. The rest of you can. But certain thoughts occur to me. Jaime could get the lot and Quinn, the smartest operator in the business, is poised right there to carry her off—the lily-white prize. He's always been a great one for keeping ahead of us. Look at all the time Simon and Brett put in on her. The results, scorn from those burning blue eyes; Quinn only had to look at her. I tell you he's clever.'

'And he's incredibly sexy!' Leigh said from the depths of her jealous despair. 'At any rate she'll know by now that she's not another Chanel.'

'And what is that supposed to mean?' Gerard Hunter glared at her in the fraught pause.

'Oh, just a little plan we cooked up together,' Sue-Ellen said uneasily.

Her father's eyes narrowed unpleasantly. 'Don't confuse Jaime with Sterling, you little fool! He's back, and he'll put paid to any of your bitchy little schemes—and what's more you'll have to pay for it. *I* won't!'

'Now, now!' Georgia exclaimed, not daring to continue this line of discussion. 'Would you mind terribly if we all be quiet?'

'My mother, are you going to pray?' asked Sue-Ellen.

'No, that wouldn't be right.'

'Why not?' Evelyn Hunter suddenly cleared her throat. A little afraid of Georgia and her daughter, she now felt disgusted with them. 'It's obvious we all regard prayer as something shameful. That might account for our lack of integrity.'

'Oh, excuse us,' Sue-Ellen murmured caustically. 'There's nothing worse than a convert.' She got up and walked to the beautiful bay window, looking out. 'How gloomy death is! How chilling! It's easy to see why people like to live dangerously and die young. I couldn't bear to grow old and sick. Grandfather from the height of his powers to this—a frail and haggard old man. It's an outrage. I wonder how Jaime is going? The King is dead, long live the Queen. In the meantime we all feel ill!'

There was nothing more said in the room.

Trembling, and trying desperately not to cry, Jaime approached the huge four-poster bed where her grandfather lay dying. She had known him for so little time. He had ignored her for almost all of her life, so she could have been expected to feel little more than compassion, the trouble was, she loved him and had loved him on encounter. Ruthless and egocentric though he was, she wanted nothing more than to have him stay with her for ever, when finally she had to admit, as she leaned over his bed, he could stand no more.

His eyes were shut and she was terrified he might be already dead. Then his hand moved on the covers and he seemed to be training all his concentration into opening his eyes. The man who had founded a splendid and flourishing corporation looked appallingly frail, more dead than alive, curiously small and pathetic for a man who stood at more than six feet. Jaime struggled to keep back her tears, but they spilled out of her eyes and one sparkling diamond splashed on to her grandfather's hand. The handsome old face was all bone now, bloodless, the silver hair stiff around his skull. It was too much, and she had never seen death before. She was tempted to bury her face in her hands to hide from the common dread, to somehow cover a whole world of regrets, but she was committed now to witness her grandfather's death. It was absolutely the most dreadful moment of her life, and the anguish was in her face. She could not bear it if he had to endure agony.

Quinn and the doctor stood close together at the far side of the room. Both of them had forgotten everything except the sight of the dying man and Jaime's tortured young face. Quinn, who had reason to hate, immediately forgave all the things that had been done to his father and his father before him. It didn't seem to matter now.

Jaime looked breakable in the restrained lighting, the concentrated essence of womanly sorrow, the lamp striking purple tints in the silky masses of her hair. He had brought her here to this. She was so young, so intensely *feeling*, he might have spared her. Her life hadn't been easy and her relatives had done everything in their power to make her uncomfortable and unwelcome since she had arrived at Falconer. But there was nothing weak or unstable about her. She had the old man's brilliance without his ruthlessness, the old man's strength without the coldness of temperament that had kept his sons and his grandchildren going beggarly for a sign of heartfelt affection. What did it matter now anyway? Man was born to heartbreak. Quinn might want to spare her, for the sight of her was tearing into him, but he knew it was impossible. Jaime would have to suffer. There was a price to be paid for everything.

A second or more later, with an indescribable effort, Rolf Hunter opened his eyes, striving to raise himself from the pillows. He was frowning, trying to see through the awful fog before his eyes as he stared straight in front of him. Jaime moved and he rasped out a single word, his face clearing miraculously, lighting up so that Jamie began to whimper in her throat.

'Rowena!' he said, pushing up, and it was impossible to mistake the loving ecstasy of his tone, the pride and the utter belief that he was face to face with his daughter.

Jaime looked down at him, taking his hand and easing him gently on to the pillows. 'I'm here, Father. Don't worry, I'm here to look after you.'

He rested back, his head turned to her, staring at her with shining eyes. 'Rowena!' he said again, marvellously eased.

Jaime lifted her head to find Quinn. She wasn't Jaime at all, but her mother, and she was content that this should be so, for it granted her grandfather a strange serenity. The expression in Quinn's black eyes descended on her like a benediction. She would never doubt the depths of his nature again. He cared for her in some way.

She sank to the floor, kneeling now beside the bed, stroking her grandfather's hand. There was the faintest smile on his mouth, every line of pain on his face eased out. She relaxed her head for a moment, even hopeful of some immense recovery, so that the doctor's words hit her like a blow:

'He's gone!'

Jaime threw up her head and saw that this was so. All her own breath seemed to leave her. It was impossible to mistake death, the emptiness. 'Oh, God!' she dropped her head on to the bed and burst into uncontrollable weeping for her grandfather's parting soul.

'Jaime, Jaime, don't. I can't bear it!' Quinn moved forward quickly and lifted her bodily away from the bed, feeling the throbbing pain in her, while Robby Burnett, his face puckered, leaned over and closed his friend's eyes. 'Go to them, Quinn. Tell them, I can't.'

'In a minute.' Quinn looked down at Jaime. He was cradling her like a child, unable to see her face buried so infinitely touchingly against him. Her teeth were chattering and she was shaking vehemently, when outside it was a blissful summer's night.

'I'll give her something,' Robby muttered over his shoulder. 'Poor old man. Poor, poor old man. Goodbye, my old friend. If any one of them says the wrong thing to me I shall strike them, and I've never hit anyone in my life.'

Quinn hesitated for a moment, then he lifted Jaime in his arms and carried her towards the door. 'I'll take Jaime to her room, then I'll go down. I don't want her exposed to them. They'll be cruel even in their pain.'

'Margo will look after her,' Robby said quietly. 'Take her there. I can make the arrangements here.'

'Thank you, Robby.'

'Listen, Quinn!'

'Yes?'

'You're a good man.'

'I've been ... lots of things!'

161

They looked at one another in silence across the great bed. 'I know the old stories. I say what I mean. You're a good man. Be kind to that child—hardly bearable the way the old fellow thought she was Rowena.'

'Yes, Rowena, offering pardon!' Quinn said sombrely. 'The only one who ever held a place in his heart. He never did see Jaime as she really is, only an extension of his daughter. Still, it gave him peace at the end. Or peace of a sort.'

Quinn glanced at the bed again, his dark face set, then he moved out through the door with his slight burden. The quivering slender body moved him profoundly. He couldn't leave her here to the tender mercies of the Hunters. With her grandfather gone, Jaime had no other friend in the house. He would take her to Rosemount. His grandmother would know how to console her grief. Never callous, he began to feel the great silence of the house. Death communicated its own message. The heirs of Sir Rolf Hunter would be no less stricken than Jaime; all of them the old man had starved of love, hardened in every possible way, so it would be necessary now to show a little of Jaime's compassion. For all of them it was the end of an era. Rolf Hunter had been an unforgettable man.

The week that followed her grandfather's funeral would always have a place in Jaime's memory. His death had stunned all of them, but immediately the will was read they all began to recover, determined to make a fight of it. It had been expected that Jaime would be richly rewarded beyond her deserts, now it seemed Sir Rolf had made an unforgivable welter of it. To the amazement of everyone, he had left her Falconer and the entire contents of the house, including the magnificent art collection. Add to that a massive bundle of shares

162

in Hunter Sterling Exploration and Hunter Sterling Land Corporation, and it was the final crack on the head.

Even at Rosemount Jaime was made aware of the family's impotent rage. It was hell, and there were necessary meetings and coldly abusive phone calls. She was torn in all directions, because she didn't want Falconer nor a fortune. As Sir Rolf Hunter's heiress, her name and photographs had found themselves into all the papers, giving of all things the Just Jaime label an enormous if temporary boost. Di, with a single phone call, had assured her of this. Jaime Gilmore might have been a nothing, but the late Sir Rolf Hunter's granddaughter was quite a different matter. The boutiques that had scorned her now could spare her all the time in the world, but she promised them nothing.

Her father had not attended the funeral. He hadn't even expressed regret when Jaime rang him that first evening at Rosemount. All he had promised was to defer his pending marriage until Jaime was free and able to travel up to Queensland. The tears running down her paper-white cheeks, Jaime didn't have it in her heart to upbraid him. It would have been hypocrisy for her father to have said he was sorry, but it seemed proper to stick with the nice old-fashioned idea of murmuring a few sympathetic words to the living. Derrick Gilmore had always loathed and detested his father-in-law : Jaime had loved him. Their views could scarcely be compatible. At that time Jaime had not been aware of her stunning inheritance, so she had given her father no news that interested him, so that finally when she hung up she wondered why she had rung at all.

'He wasn't in the least sorry,' she had murmured to Mrs Sterling, and Margo Sterling had touched her

163

head gently with a wry: 'I daresay!'

The days passed, of course, but Jaime was never to forget them. Quinn, however, was Quinn, always going forward, never back. She couldn't have done without him, for he soon put an end to all the harsh words that were offered to her by her relations. She could never have borne them unflinchingly without Quinn, for he seemed to find her a quick way out of all her difficulties. He had now taken on the role of conscientious and supremely capable big brother who went right out of his way to dispose of all her problems, as though she were a precious and incompetent semi-invalid, which for that week she was.

When she began to recover she approached him about Falconer. He spent most of his evenings at Rosemount, which delighted his grandmother, but Jaime had never seen him alone. It was a deliberate manoeuvre and she had forewarned Mrs Sterling so that that lady retired early, allowing Jaime to corner Quinn's entire attention. The night was a blaze of stars, the breeze coming in off the water, so they sat in the semi-dark of the verandah to escape the heat, Jaime on the cushioned lounger, Quinn a few feet from her, maddeningly relaxed.

'Quinn,' she said purposefully.

'Hmm?'

'There's something I want to talk to you about.'

'Oh, my God!' he said.

'You told me to tell you if there was anything bothering me.'

'It's plain there is now. Go ahead, my lady!'

'About Falconer . . .'

'Lordy!' he interjected, his teeth a flash of white in his dark face.

'Are you going to listen to me or not?'

'Baby, I'm so tired,' he sighed.

'Are you? It doesn't seem possible, you're such a miracle of energy.'

'It just happens I am.'

'Then come and sit beside me.'

'No, thanks, Jaime. You said you want to *talk*.'

'I don't want Falconer!' she said bluntly. 'It's too big, it's too beautiful, it's too valuable. It could only hold unhappy memories for me.'

'How sad. Tell me, what do you intend to do with it?'

'Practically anything but live in it.'

'May I make a merciful suggestion?' he enquired.

'Please do.'

'Sell it to your Uncle Gerard for a fair price. It's always been his home, you know.'

'Are you trying to say that Grandfather was unfair?' she asked.

'Not *trying* to say, darling girl. With time and forgetfulness I might change my tune. Obnoxious as Gerard undoubtedly is I feel sorry for him.'

'So do I. In fact, I don't know why I didn't think of it myself.'

'These haven't been great days for you. Tell me, what do you weigh now?'

'You'll still be able to carry me,' she told him.

'Much more important, I might be able to make love to you. You look like a little girl, all curled up there. Shall I approach your nice uncle?'

'Would you?'

'I have to work with him. It isn't easy. There's no way of knowing how he will react initially. But I'm sure it will eventually be arranged.'

'That's the house,' she said.

'And there's more?' Quinn asked wryly.

165

'Uncle Gerard is a very rich man. I can't feel *too* sorry for him. The art collection, the *Australian* art collection, I have definite ideas about. It's a complete history of our art from the colonial days to the outstanding artists of our day. I don't feel entitled to hoard it up like a miser with his gold. It's part of the national heritage. I would like everyone to see it. What did you say?'

'Nothing!' he said blandly. 'I'm just numb. Keep going, Jaime, I'll just sit here and admire you.'

'I think I'd like it to go on permanent loan to the national art galleries.'

'That's splendid. I think you'd better keep the Renoirs and the Picassos.'

'I'm serious, Quinn,' she rebuked.

'So am I. You're the only benevolent Hunter I've met. A strange child in a strange land. What about the fantastic assemblage of antiques?'

'I thought I'd let each member of the family select a favourite piece. I want the Oriental vases and the portrait of my mother. What's left can go up for public auction, and the proceeds can go to medical research foundations. My mother died in childbirth. It was touch and go for me, I believe. I'd like some of the money to be set aside for that kind of thing.'

Quinn sat up. 'I said I was tired, but you seem to have brought about an incredible renascence. Is it possible you want to finish up with nothing?'

'I have all those shares,' she pointed out.

'So you do.' He rocked back precariously and put his arms behind his head. 'God knows what the old man would have thought of this.'

'He wouldn't have approved?'

'He was never known to give anything away that couldn't go down as a tax deduction. You're undoubtedly the finest, purest Hunter I've known.'

'I wanted to talk to you about it,' she confided.

'Is that why Grandmamma went to bed?'

'We talk practically all the time. No secrets.'

'Yes, you're no longer the child of Rowena. You're Jaime, and Jaime wouldn't let anyone suffer.'

'Don't entangle me in all the sad, old stories,' she said. 'Are you sure you know who I am?'

'Jaime, the witch,' he responded.

'Within limits. I can't even get you to sit beside me.'

'No, you can't!' he said crisply. 'I've seen all your fearful little violet-eyed glances, the ideas they've put into your head. Black-hearted Sterling carrying off the heiress. The powerfully cruel eagle with the pathetic little lamb.'

'You have been mentioned, yes,' she said truthfully, trying not to remember exactly what was said. 'There's no need to even go on with the engagement.'

'Particularly when you're going to give everything away!'

He sounded so vastly ironical that Jaime swept off the lounger shaking with the urge to hit him. 'Oh no, you don't!' he said, catching her around the waist. 'You're my business partner anyway, and you're going to make me rich!'

'You *are* rich. That's the only thing that confuses me, but some men are power-mad.' She was facing him, speaking softly but intensely, his fingers hard about her waist.

'No news, Jaime. I'm power-mad at the minute!' In seconds he pulled her down on to his knees, making it seem the most natural, the most dangerous thing in the world. 'You're absolutely determined about all this?'

'Absolutely.'

'But you decline to go on with the engagement that never had a chance to get off the ground?'

'I have certain information that you're just using me!'

'There is that possibility,' he said suavely.

'Thank you, Quinn, for admitting it.'

'I'm not admitting anything. I'm trying to agree with you. It's what you want, isn't it?'

'Would you please let me go?'

'Definitely not. I was a fool not to have thought of it before, but you seemed so fragile.'

'Is it true?' she insisted.

'What?' He stared into her flower face. 'Oh, I see ... Am I using you. What a dreadful way to put it! For one thing, Jaime, I can't resist you, but I wouldn't be telling the truth if I said I was unmindful of the advantages. My maternal grandmother was French. Doesn't that mean something to you? Marriages of convenience and all that, sensible, long-lasting arrangements. That appeals to me. Besides, you're going to be famous.'

'Depend on it.'

'Oh, I am. I never back long shots. I like that dress. It shimmers in this light. Yes, you're going to be the designer to end all designers. They're my pearls, aren't they?'

'Yes, they are!' She shivered as his hand touched her bare skin.

'They're the new length, or so they told me,' he observed idly, 'and they look good with a deep V. You're so beautiful, Jaime, you were bound to complicate things.'

'If you're not going to let me up do you mind if I make myself more comfortable?'

'I'm hoping you will, because you're not going anywhere. I mean it—relax. You'd do anything for me, Jaime, wouldn't you?'

'I never at any time said that!' she half whispered.

'But you mean it, don't you?'

She rested against him, her breathing deep and urgent. 'Do you know what Grandfather once said to me? There's nothing easier than pretending love to a woman.'

'I'd find it equally impossible to pretend I wanted a woman when I didn't. Your grandfather was a wicked old man, God rest his soul!'

'It happens, though, Quinn,' she said gravely.

'Shut up for a while, would you, because I'm quite normal and you're the most desirable creature I'm ever likely to meet.'

'Are you saying that with a thread of self-contempt? You have such a voice for inflections. You can manage to convey anything.'

'I said, let's not talk. Turn your head up, Jaime. I don't want to hurt you.'

'I have a feeling you will soon,' she sighed.

'And that's bad? It seems such a long time, Jaime.'

'Yes.' She spoke so softly her words just melted into the darkness. Maybe she didn't even say them, but felt them. It had seemed an eternity. Her smile had faded and her face was very still.

'Nowhere to go, Jaime?' he murmured with low mockery. His hand that encircled her nape suddenly slipped under her chin, forcing her head up. 'Your skin is as luminous as that string of pearls or the soft summer moonlight. I knew at the beginning where it would lead to!'

She was silent, just staring up at him, seeing the sparkle of his eyes in the scented gloom. Then all at once she was trembling violently, with a desire she couldn't hide. He gathered her right up against him with a hard deliberation, lowering his head on a shattering path to her mouth. Her breath fluttered and she was pervaded with such urgent sensations that it was like some powerful rising storm, a quickening she couldn't control, with only Quinn holding the key to whatever path they were travelling. The very darkness seemed to be burning, crackling with a mounting intensity.

'Jaime!' he said barely audibly, twisting his hand through her hair as his mouth lifted a little, lingering, learning every contour of her face and throat. She was just a slender blur against him, her heart pounding heavily. If he wanted her to believe he loved her, he was succeeding. All she could think of was recapturing his mouth, moving her head blindly, as if the most totally important thing in the world was to seek the source of such exquisite excitement.

They might have been at the very core of a pulsing circle ringed with fire, the breeze cooling her heated skin, but never the echoing wildness in her blood. His mouth was warm and hard, faultless in its task of arousal, his hands positive, insistent, caressing, sure of her, sure of fashioning her into whatever he wanted. If it was folly to be taken over so completely, it was something she wanted too badly to resist. There wasn't a shadow between them but a remorseless passion, Jaime's head thrown back in a beautiful abandon, his hand caught in her hair, while he continued to kiss her in a brilliant devastation.

'Jaime!' He lifted his head slowly, his breath uneven. 'No, don't stop.'

'I'm just tormenting both of us.'

'I don't care!'

'I do. Believe me, I'm going to take very good care of you.'

'Oh, *why*?' she said, sounding mortally deprived and not in the least thankful.

'In this case, because you're just twenty years old!'

'Does it ever occur to you I'm a woman?'

'What a fool question! That's what's causing all the trouble. Sit up and behave. I want to go on with this quite shockingly, but we've done enough dallying for now. Let's go inside.' He lifted her off his knee with tremendous decision and stood up.

'God, how confusing!' Jaime groaned. 'Here I am maddened with passion and you're as retiring as an inoffensive, sanctimonious parson.'

'I should ravish you for that!' he said, and dropped a violent kiss on her mouth. 'I'm a gentleman by nature, Jaime, just don't keep flinging yourself at me.'

'I never get the chance,' she said derisively.

'I wouldn't care, but first you have to tell me, do you love me?'

She stood looking up at him. He didn't seem serious. 'You might just as well ask me if I trust you!'

'Of course, I forgot. You don't!'

'Quinn?' She drew nearer him and touched his sleeve, dismayed by the hard note in his voice. 'I was only fooling, you know.'

'You fool too much!'

'So do you.'

'Yes, I suppose so. You look like a girl who's practically been kissed senseless.'

'Which was considerably less than I felt like.'

'You are modern, Jaime!' he drawled.

She moved back a step and he followed her. 'I said *felt* like. Feelings aren't actions.'

'Really? Perhaps we'd better stay here and explore this dazzling new world we've just found.'

'No, we'll go inside and I can see your black scowl!'

In the hallway Jaime turned her head back over her shoulder. 'Do you think you'll be able to make Derry's wedding? He does so want you to come.'

His dark face was very handsome, very seeking and alive. He adjusted the collar of his shirt, a faint smile on his mouth. 'Bless him! And to think I didn't know him all these years!'

'Sometimes I hate you!' she said truthfully, but she smiled, her violet eyes very soft and tender.

'That's good!' He reached out and touched her cheek. 'I don't like you either, from time to time. As for Derry, maybe I can escape for the weekend. I'll certainly try. When are you leaving?'

'Wednesday. I thought I'd have a few days as a sort of pick-me-up.'

'Believe me, you don't need one. *I* do!'

'Alcohol's not the answer, Quinn,' she said with sweet maliciousness.

'It might be tonight. Get me a drink, you violet-eyed witch. I deserve one!'

CHAPTER NINE

JAIME turned to answer yet another battery of questions. The ceremony was over and the fifty and more guests were revolving around the gallery where the reception was being held. The air was buzzing with conversation, as far as Jaime could make out, mostly about her. Overnight she had become a celebrity, the ornament of the evening, and she had dressed the part with beautiful unaccustomed extravagance in black silk chiffon printed with huge roses and peonies in Persian blue and rose, with gold and silver leaves. She had designed it as a one-shouldered toga and Di and Marike between them had run it up for her. She wore nothing around her neck, but silver pendant earrings set with turquoise and pearls. It was now her enormous responsibility to dress the part if she wished to add lustre to her own label.

Most of the guests were known to her except for Gayle's friends, the artistic community that lived and worked on the beautiful Coast, and a few of her father's best clients. They had been dumbfounded to read her story in the papers, but now they were ready to talk about it. To spring into the national spotlight with Hunter Sterling, one of the biggest enterprises in the country, and Sir Rolf Hunter Jaime's grandfather—it had come as an enormous shock to everyone. Derry had never breathed a word and he was a colossal gossip. That he had kept such a secret to himself seemed unbelievable.

Jaime was besieged from the moment she arrived. What was life like at the top? After a while she began

173

to feel a prisoner of her newly glamorous background, though she tried to sparkle and look interested, assuming what would later become her public face. Gayle was the real surprise. Knowing her father and his predilection for good-looking women, well covered if possible, she had been unprepared for Gayle's tall, thin figure, the soft copper hair and the goodly sprinkling of freckles. Gayle would never entrance the senses, but she was intelligent and articulate and made the most of herself to the extent that she appeared attractive. Somehow her father had had the good sense to see through to the essential Gayle, with her clean, strong mind and her ability to inspire contentment.

It had come as a tremendous relief to Jaime to discover that Gayle was very much in love with her father. The marriage ceremony, to Jaime's further surprise, was performed in a church and it was heartening to see her father take it all very seriously when they had had many an argument on religion. His views had been quite straightforward then. In a very short time Gayle appeared to have worked wonders, and from the look of happiness about them tonight, things could only go on improving. Gayle at their first meeting had been very nervous under her nice easy manner, but Jaime found her pretty nearly perfect and said so. Gayle loved her father, and from his attitude he appeared to regard her warmly in return. Jaime could only be happy for them. In her own quiet way, Gayle was also sharpening his ambitions, and had become very involved in the art scene herself since her arrival on the Coast, and Jaime felt almost breathless to see what this new stimulus would lead to.

Derrick Gilmore was a very good artist, the trouble was that his whole life had been drastically upset and altered as a young man, robbing him of any real incentive. Jaime, though he would never have told her and foolishly imagined she didn't know, reminded him unbearably of Rowena. Though she had inspired his best work, her portrait, and he loved her, her presence never eased Rowena from his conscious mind : Rowena and her father, Rolf Hunter, for whom he had always felt such hatred that it swamped him. Gayle, who he feared he hadn't even noticed at the beginning, was steadily changing his attitudes to everything. He was almost tranquil and looked incredibly youthful, as some fair men remained for a large part of their lives.

It gave Jaime great pleasure to see her father looking so well, and if she had to surrender him to another woman, she could feel truly glad about Gayle. Tavia, now, would have been another matter, and Tavia surprisingly had been invited and came to the reception but not the ceremony. It was the unanimous opinion that Derry had been fortunate to win such an attractive and intelligent young wife.

It was a Friday night. It was a party, they were enjoying one another's company enormously, celebrating the marriage of a dear friend. No one seemed in the least inclined to go home any more than Gayle and Derrick wanted to depart. The leading figures of the artistic community were there, the painters, the potters and the craftsmen, so they were content to raid the excellent buffet, grab another drink and return quickly with their own pertinent or controversial comments. Not a soul looking at Jaime, so beautiful and argumentative, could have guessed at her other preoccupations and the bitter disappointment she was feeling. The blazing anticipation with which she had dressed had given way to a becoming loss of confidence in her powers of seduction. It had been an enthralling idea to think Quinn might be slightly in love with her, and the thought had her so buoyant that she was floating, now with every passing minute it seemed she was wrong. He had never left Sydney, though he had sent a handsome present that endeared him to Gayle from a distance. Meantime Jaime was discovering she was leading two lives, stimulating the conversation and mourning Quinn's absence. She couldn't enjoy herself no matter what anyone thought, but she owed it to Derry and Gayle to scintillate.

The gallery was overflowing with people, yet she might have been alone on a desert island. Gayle, catching sight of her momentarily betraying face, excused herself from her group and started towards Jaime, who clearly heard not a word her highly entranced companion was saying to her. Gayle smiled at him and waved him away, taking Jaime's arm.

'You're the sensation of the evening. Our celebrity.'

'Possibly,' agreed Jaime.

'Also you're so extravagantly beautiful I'm frightened to stand beside you. The only thing is, I'm a good reader of faces and I just caught your expression.'

'I'm enjoying myself, Gayle!' Jaime protested smilingly. 'I would never have missed your wedding for the world.'

'I know you really mean that, Jaime, and it means a lot to me. Your friend, Mr Sterling, can't be coming.'

'It doesn't seem likely now,' she agreed.

'I imagine he's an extremely busy man.'

'I can't pretend that's not true.'

'You're pretty badly in love with him?' Gayle suggested, risking getting put in her place.

'Is it showing?' Jaime said wryly.

'Only to me perhaps, being very much in love myself.'

'Ah well,' said Jaime, 'don't let it throw a shadow on

us. Derry looks very happy, Gayle. Thank you for that. I think he can do with a new family background. He was never happy with the old.'

'No, and he kept remarkably quiet about it. Odd in Derry. The whole story is fantastic. I expect you can't believe it's happening, Jaime.'

'The money doesn't mean very much to me, Gayle.'

Gayle nodded. 'No, I don't think I'd want too much money myself. Great wealth must be frightening. You up there with everyone resentful and envious trying to pull you down. One would feel so exposed. Tavia's being very friendly, isn't she?'

'Tavia's a deep one.'

'She was very fond of your father.'

'Indeed yes!' Jaime murmured, wondering if Gayle knew exactly how fond. 'You've shown some skill interesting him in marriage.'

'I'm an old-fashioned girl!' Gayle smiled. 'Even Derry had to see that. Anyway, he didn't see it coming until it was too late.'

Derrick, however, saw their smiles and he came towards them, slipping an arm around each one of them. 'How are my girls?'

'Some people have all the luck!'

'Don't they now!' Derrick bent his head sideways and kissed Jaime's cheek. 'You look extremely beautiful tonight. What an exquisite piece of material!' he added with the artist's eye. 'You've handled it just the right way—simply. You seem to have grown up and gone away from me.'

'No, Derry!' Her beautiful eyes were very tender. 'We'll always be just as we are now!'

For a moment her father stared into her face, completely in the grip of the past. Gayle's smile wavered at the strained intensity of his gaze. 'Darling?' she said, but he never even heard her.

Those very words had been said to him twenty years before, and he had never seen her alive again. For a second he was forced to relive the old tearing agony, the blind, hopeless, never-ending alleyways of pain. Straight out of heaven, right into hell, and everyone expected him to shine. He had been left aimless, *aimless*, for twenty long years. Jaime, familiar with that hard tormented look, wasn't surprised or upset when he dropped his arms abruptly and walked away from them.

'What happened?' Gayle asked in bewilderment, turning slowly towards Jaime, her amber eyes frightened.

'Nothing to worry about, Gayle!' Jaime said kindly.

Gayle stood twisting her wedding ring, and tried to regain the golden glow of the evening. 'Can't you tell me? I've never seen Derry like that before.'

'There's nothing to tell. Derry was seeing a ghost, perhaps. Do you believe in them?'

'If they looked like you, maybe. Your mother was a very beautiful woman, wasn't she?'

'She died when I was born,' said Jaime. 'I have no memories of her, Gayle, only a portrait. It could be me.'

'And Derry never told me. All that part of his life he's kept rigidly bottled up, locked away inside of him.'

'If it's any consolation to you, Gayle, he never told me either. But what are you looking so melancholy about? These isolated little incidents pass. You won't experience them at all when I'm not around.'

'I suppose we're never free of the past,' Gayle said, meditatively.

'I'm sure now that's right,' said Jaime, thinking of her grandfather's last moments. 'The thing to do is subordinate it, and you're just the girl to do it.'

'Eventually!' Gayle said wryly, struck with a problem she hadn't been aware of.

'You love my father, don't you?' asked Jaime.

'Oh yes!'

'Well then. Whoever claimed anything was easy— and just to prove life goes on, here comes Derry again!'

He came back to them smiling, as if nothing at all had happened; no explanations, just a lift of his elegant hands. 'Gayle, my love, you've got to come right over here and settle a point. Jaime darling, excuse us for a moment. Gayle can talk like a bibliography on any painter you can name in any part of the world.'

For a second Gayle didn't respond, then she wound both her arms around her husband's sleeve. 'Can you give me a clue?'

'Local.'

'That's easy!'

Naturally Jaime's earlier admirer saw the moment to return bearing two glasses of champagne. Jaime accepted a glass gratefully, very nearly on the point of tears. Weddings were emotional events and her father's momentary lapse had assuredly upset Gayle, though she had tried to rally. Her companion was telling her she had the most beautiful eyes in the world; one hand held up the wall behind her, trapping her, bent slightly towards her, viewing her steadily. She couldn't remember what his name was. It could have been Eric or it could have been Ian. It emphatically wasn't Quinn.

Then slowly and painfully Quinn's dark handsome face began to superimpose itself on the tanned pleasant face of the man before her. Jaime found herself staring, the pupils of her eyes distending, in turn disturbing her companion to such a degree that his hand trembled. He had settled on Jaime the moment he had caught a glimpse of her in the church, long before he knew she was a very wealthy girl. Now with her blue-violet eyes intent on him, he almost passed out. What was so astonishing was that a friend had just told him he was wasting his time. A girl like Jaime with money as well was out of this world. Certainly out of his reach. Now her beautiful violet eyes were trained on him, confusing and exciting him. The next second he realised she wasn't even seeing him, for she blinked rapidly.

'That's the strangest thing!' she said uncertainly.

'What?' he asked, baffled and disappointed beyond mere words. This time her eyes went beyond him, widening, and the colour swept into her lovely face, like a fire suddenly lit inside of her. 'Oh, excuse me,' she said with a gentle, eager rush. 'A friend of mine has just arrived.'

Ian Gibson turned his head, of course, and his hopes were killed dead, pathetic now as it happened, and he wasn't a bad-looking man. Gayle and her new husband were greeting the smoothest, most sophisticated-looking character Ian had ever seen. Very tall, very lean, a classy dresser, his head tilted towards Gayle, who was blushing and laughing; a careless, handsome, arrogant devil, slightly foreign-looking, with black eyes that now lit on Jaime. The miracle of a girl in her delectable dress, the girl who had seemed so young and eager, was now greeting the stranger with an equally cool, sophisticated poise. Obviously they belonged together and Ian felt desperately envious. Quite a few people had broken off in their conversations to stare and Ian caught the name Sterling.

Of course, that explained it. A man who looked and talked like that just had to be somebody, a real big wheel. Ian couldn't figure what lots of money did, but it did. For the first time he began to pay attention to

180

the girl he had come with, who wasn't tearfully sad anyway.

With the arrival of Quinn, and the consequent introductions, the reception gained a valuable new impetus. He was stared up and down, devoured by the women, and suffered it all with great charm, never once passing his hands in front of his eyes as Jaime did on more than one occasion. With a harsh stab of reality and no sense of resentment, she was made to stand back and observe the immense sexual attraction he held for other women. There was no question of anyone going home now unless Hugo, who owned and ran the gallery, turned out the lights, and he obviously didn't want to. Contacts were important and 'good old Derry' had an heiress for a daughter and a friend in Quinn Sterling of Hunter Sterling, who had kissed the tips of Gayle's fingers the moment he arrived, making that new bride swim with pleasure. It had to be some Gallic blood in his background, Hugo reasoned. He's never seen another man do it quite like that, except maybe Charles Boyer in those old movies.

Shortly after midnight, Gayle and Derrick decided to leave and after that they all got away fairly swiftly. With the newlyweds staying overnight at the best hotel on the Coast, Jaime was free to go back to the beach house. With Quinn so very much in demand, she had scarcely spoken two consecutive words to him. Indeed, although his brilliant eyes strayed over her frequently, he had seemed another person, considering her memories of their last meeting. It was impossible to read what went on behind those pitch-black eyes, and now with all her confidence abating she wasn't even going to try. She might have looked her very best and made all that effort mostly for him, yet he looked extraordinarily unmoved, quite relaxed, with no more than an ordinary passing interest in her appearance. He was scarcely to be borne unless he was a split personality.

Over the short distance home in the hire car she didn't even look at him, or turn her head. He had explained his delay, of course. His position gave him any number of excellent alibis. Who could be certain if he saw the Minister or not? If he did, it was very good of him to come anyway, and if he didn't, he had only just made it. Her mood of rejection and despondency had set in accompanied by the moral post-wedding-reception blues. Marriage wasn't always the answer. She only hoped Gayle would bring an illuminating quality to hers. Her father wasn't an easy man to know, and that summing up wasn't only limited to her father. She was just thinking Quinn was a stranger.

'Are you going to invite me in?' he asked smoothly, the moment they arrived.

'Are you certain you want to?' she said coolly. 'I thought this was a mercy mission.'

He ignored her. 'I'd like some black coffee, thank you, Jaime. Maybe a sandwich. I missed lunch and dinner, you know, all on your account.'

'Did you really?'

'Is there absolutely anything you'll believe of me? To the good, that is!'

She fumbled with the front door key and his hand shot out and took it from her, inserted it into the lock and turned the spring. Jaime swept ahead of him, switching on the lights. There was a wild carnation tint over her delicate cheekbones, not just a blusher, but quickening blood. In a few days with the glorious wash of sun, her skin had turned to a gleaming gold again, and the devastating excitement she was feeling coloured her eyes almost purple. It was vastly foolish the way she let Quinn agitate and upset her.

She put her evening purse and her floating chiffon stole down and went to the sliding glass doors that led on to the balcony and provided an incomparable view of the ocean. A moment more and the lovely sea breeze came into the room, with the fresh tang of salt fluttering the curtains. She glanced back at Quinn almost defiantly and caught him regarding her with a certain amount of dark arrogance.

'I learned a lot tonight,' he said in an attacking voice. 'You're fairly provocative with everyone.'

'You're mad!' she responded. 'I'd have to try desperately to remember one face!'

'How about that chap—Gibson, wasn't it? The one who had you pinned to the wall when I arrived.'

Jaime's delicate nostrils flared and her eyebrows shot up. 'I should be able to remember him, but I can't.'

'I'm surprised to hear that. You were certainly staring up at him very agreeably.'

'You couldn't be jealous?'

'No,' he said contemptuously with the cool arrogance that exasperated her and threw a corresponding switch in her.

'Do you really want that coffee or a fight?' she demanded.

'You're very aggressive,' he said narrowly, his black eyes glinting.

'I waited all evening for you!' she burst out, surprising herself. She hadn't meant to say that.

'I *told* you!' he said impatiently. 'It was impossible to make the early flight. Swinging a big business venture doesn't go hand in hand with pleasing oneself!'

Jaime shook her head as if she didn't want to discuss it any more. 'I'll make the coffee. We've chicken and ham. Which?'

'As a matter of fact, both. There was very little left of that buffet.'

'Yes, I know, and it cost the earth!' Jaime said, suddenly distressed on his account. In fact a wave of remarkable, inexplicable desolation came over her. She dashed her hands in front of her eyes and turned away. She felt she had to. There was no denying it. Quinn unsettled her so badly that just being alone with him gave her a bad time.

'What damn game are you playing now?' he demanded, covering the distance between them with devastating speed. He swung her about and stared down into her face.

'I'm not used to being manhandled!' she said shortly.

'Then there's no time like the present. Forget the blasted coffee. I'm not in the mood anyway.'

'Why are you so angry?' she challenged him, her blue eyes blazing.

'Aren't you?'

'Yes, I am, and I don't know why. I hope Derry's going to be happy. You scarcely said two words to me all night.'

'You're very demanding, aren't you?'

'Quite possibly. I thought you enjoyed my company?'

'If so I'm not the only one.'

'You're jealous!' she accused.

His lean fingers bit into her shoulders. 'If it were only that simple! There's a considerable difference between being jealous and wanting to turn you over my knee. You need taking in hand, Jaime. You're too beautiful for your own good, and you're so vital that you really affect people. You're going to need a strong hand and a man a lot older than you. No ordinary run-

184

of-the-mill young man would do. You'd lead him a sorry dance!'

'And you're the man with a difference, I suppose?'

'Careful, I'm not playing.'

'As a matter of fact neither am I,' she retorted. 'You're pretty remarkable at that. To think I was in the odd position this afternoon of longing for you to arrive! Now you're here you just want to snarl at me.'

'I'll show you what I want to do!' He lifted her clean off the floor and walked backwards with her to the couch, pinning her body.

'What's got into you?' she asked faintly, thinking it advisable to retreat.

He dismissed the violet alarm of her eyes, threading his hand through her hair experimentally, whether to pull it or what, Jaime couldn't tell. 'You're untamed, aren't you?' he asked abruptly.

'I prefer to be,' she said clearly.

'Since it's not going to happen for very much longer, make the most of it.'

'How's the family?' she flashed at him. 'Leigh and Sue-Ellen?'

'Coming right out of it. I saw Leigh briefly yesterday. She looked a picture. She was in to see her father.'

'I'm sure she continued down the corridor to you.'

'As a matter of fact she did.'

'Well done, then!'

'I'm not used to young women like you,' said Quinn, his eyes sliding down the length of her, the slender young body, the exquisite long legs outlined by the tautened chiffon.

'Then you should be glad of a little variety!' she said shakily.

'I wasn't looking for trouble.'

'Neither was I.'

'You've got it!' He looked hard and reckless, though she was seeing his face through a shimmering haze.

'It's fairly obvious I bring out the barbarian in you,' she blurted.

'What little there is. But yes, I agree. There's something about you that makes me want to hurt you. Move your hand away from your face. What is it, some kind of protection?'

'I won't!' she said firmly.

'You have noticed I'm stronger than you.'

'You're a bully as well!'

'Now and again. You'll only get hurt struggling, so stop it. I haven't time for it anyway. Argue as you will, you love me!'

'No.'

'*No?* That sort of an answer needs proving. Such an exquisite dress. What a pity to crush it!'

'You're perfectly well aware it's uncrushable.'

'Is that an invitation? Well then!'

'Don't you dare touch me!' she said wildly, safe if she kept talking.

'Face it, Jaime. I'll do anything I have to to get you!'

'Aren't my feelings important?'

For answer he took hold of her in a hard practised manner. 'There's got to be one boss, and we're going to settle this, my poor frightened baby. It's unfair to take advantage of you, but I have to. I can't even understand myself these days!'

'You'd better!' she warned with her very last breath of resistance. Her blood was on fire, answering the violence of emotion in him.

He grasped the back of her head very deliberately. 'Let me look at you. Just who *are* you anyway?'

'I'm Jaime!' she said passionately, to establish her

186

identity once and for all. 'Just Jaime, and I don't mean any blasted label!'

'You're mine!' he said with no trace of ardency but implacably, twisting her head back and kissing her mouth violently.

She began to struggle, slipping sideways on the couch so that Quinn was half leaning over her. 'Go on, deny it. If you want to, you'd better do it now!'

A volcanic hard recklessness was upon him, a queer tautness in his expression. 'No, I don't want to!' she whispered, visibly relenting. There could be no other way for her. So deeply in love, she was now trying to subdue the antagonisms she had invited. She was unaware of the radiant tenderness that invaded her eyes, the soft natural yielding of her body. It came so suddenly, this surrender, that it completely flooded her being.

Quinn didn't move for a second, his black eyes anything but tranquil. There was a devil in him and she had aroused it. Now she was looking shatteringly submissive, a contrary little enchantress, as fragile as a flower, as brilliant as a jewel. He didn't trust her, but the compulsion to make love to her was taking control of him.

Jaime drew in her breath, lifted her arms and linked them around Quinn's neck, forestalling his anger. 'Don't look at me like that. You frighten me.'

'Do I?' The glittery look eased just a fraction. 'I'm sorry. Quite easily I could strangle you and I would, only I've wanted you from the very beginning.'

'You'd better have me, then,' she said gently. 'Don't you think so?'

'Who'd want to marry you off so soon?'

'It was bound to happen. Predictable.' All the while

she was lifting her mouth to his, overcome by a sweet and piercing exultation. It was wondrous to take the initiative, but it wasn't for long. One moment he held back, then he forced her head back against his shoulder; kissing her with a driving need he didn't bother to hide. It was scarcely endurable, the soft searing sensations speeding through her, the beautiful, terrible rhythm of it all. The mysterious knowable, unknowable world of Quinn.

She was lost and any other consideration never even surfaced. When he freed her mouth briefly, she murmured broken little endearments, indulging herself endlessly, telling him in every way possible that she loved him. She was so ravishingly helpless, yet so flamelike, that soon there was nothing else for Quinn to do but pull away with the kind of steely strength that marked him.

'I think it's time for me to go back to the hotel,' he said, grasping her hair.

'Darling, you're here with me.'

He drew away from her treacherous sweetness, sat up and pushed her filmy skirt aside.

'Oh God, I don't know what to do about you!' Jaime moaned.

'You won't have to for long. We'll see Gayle and your father off tomorrow, then we'll go home.'

She leaned over, burrowing her head against his side. 'That's a tumultuous back-to-front proposal. You told me you want to marry me, but you haven't said you loved me.'

'Yes, I know.'

'Are you going to?'

'I'd never get back to the hotel,' he said dryly, not nearly so calm as he appeared.

'Who cares?' she said, and flung her arms around

him, hugging his taut frame, feeling the indecision in him then the final rejection.

Quinn stood up, turning away from her, straightening his tie as if he were about to go into a Board meeting. It was time to gather himself. She was startled at the way he could turn such powerful emotions on and off when she could hardly stand because she was trembling so violently.

At the door he relaxed, sliding an arm around her and dropping a brief parting kiss on her head. 'My beautiful Jaime. You must be tired and I've kept you up too long.'

'And you didn't get your coffee.'

'Judging by your earlier reactions you might have thrown it at me.' He held the door, looking out at the sparkling stars. 'What a beautiful night!'

She slipped herself under his shoulder. 'I feel as though you've pulled down a star for me.'

'You deserve another kiss for that,' he said tautly. 'I'm not earthbound myself.'

'Out of the question when you want someone so badly!'

'Jaime?' he said against her mouth.

'Yes?'

'I love you. You're what I've wanted all my life.'

'That sounds sweeter to me than the lovely music of the sea.'

'Just one thing. You'll never escape me. That I swear!'

'Who said I'll ever want to?' she whispered, shocked.

'It pays to know what you're getting into. I'm the man in possession, remember that.'

'And don't think I'm going to wait long,' she murmured.

'You won't have to. Whatever life holds for us, we're ready. What happens to you, happens to me. A partnership no one is going to dissolve!'

Beyond them the white sandhills were lit to a radiance. The surf rolled in, unstoppable, rushing up on to the sand like long bolts of silk. So inevitable the tide. So perfectly ordained Jaime's destiny.

Titles available this month in the
Mills & Boon ROMANCE Series

FLY BEYOND THE SUNSET *by Anne Hampson*
Faun was a perfectly competent airline pilot — so why, when she crash-landed in the Borneo jungle, did Clive Tarrant have to be on board to make things worse?

FLAMINGO MOON *by Margaret Pargeter*
When Eve arrived at Raoul DuBare's house in the Camargue, he threw her out literally. But Eve came back . . . .

THE LION OF QUIMERA *by Amanda Doyle*
Teresa thought she had applied for a governess's job in Spain, so how had she ended up on Quimera, off the South American coast, and tyrannised over by an imposing Marques?

PINEAPPLE GIRL *by Betty Neels*
A grateful patient gave Eloise a pineapple, which she promptly dropped at Timon van Zeilst's feet — and lost her heart at the same time!

PORTRAIT OF JAIME *by Margaret Way*
Jaime's grandfather, whom she have never seen, had sent for her. But if she went, she would be in Quinn Sterling's power . . . .

A TRIAL MARRIAGE *by Anne Mather*
Rachel was eighteen and Jake twenty years older — rich, sophisticated, cynical. Could they ever by happy together?

THE WRONG MAN TO LOVE *by Roberta Leigh*
Samantha's inheritance brought her nothing but disaster, for because of it she met Zachary Farrell — and he had no time for her at all!

TEMPLE OF THE MOON *by Sara Craven*
A trip to Yucatan should have solved all Gabrielle's problems, but instead she encountered a new one; the disturbing Shaun Lennox . . . .

ACROSS A CROWDED ROOM *by Lilian Peake*
Only one man — Rosco Hamden — could save Lisette from disaster. But could she pay his price?

FRASER'S BRIDE *by Elizabeth Graham*
Everyone said Lara would make the perfect wife for Jerry. But she fell in love with his brother Matt, who didn't want her!

Mills & Boon Romances
— all that's pleasureable in Romantic Reading!

Available November 1977 — Only 40p each

IMPORTANT NEWS! *Plus a personal invitation to join the exciting NEW —*

Mills & Boon Romance CLUB

YOUR VERY OWN MONTHLY MAGAZINE

NOTHING TO PAY! MEMBERSHIP IS FREE TO REGULAR READERS!

IMAGINE the *pleasure* and *security* of having ALL your favourite *Mills & Boon* romantic fiction delivered right to *your* home, absolutely POST FREE... straight off the press! No waiting! No more disappointments! All this PLUS all the latest news of *new books* and *top-selling authors* in your own monthly MAGAZINE... PLUS *regular* big CASH SAVINGS... PLUS lots of wonderful, strictly-limited, *members-only* SPECIAL OFFERS! All these exclusive benefits can be *yours*–right NOW– simply by joining the exciting NEW *Mills & Boon* ROMANCE CLUB. Post form for *FREE* full-colour leaflet. It costs nothing. HURRY!

POST FREE DELIVERY Direct to your home

SPECIAL OFFERS For members only!

Plus–all these **EXCLUSIVE BENEFITS**
- Big cash savings on selected books!
- Advance news of all new titles.
- No waiting! No more disappointments!

NO OBLIGATION TO JOIN UNLESS YOU WISH!

 CUT OUT

*DETACH AND POST COUPON BELOW FOR **FREE** DESCRIPTIVE LEAFLET!*

192